MINEHUNTI
PATROL BOATS
AND LOGISTICS

Illustrations: Lluis Adell i Jaumandreu, Camil Busquets, Douglas A. Cromby, Octavio Díez Cámara, Jorge Flethes Serrano, Santiago García Goya, Hanny & Leo Van Ginderen, Jon Godsell, Antonio Moreno García, Marc Piché, Diego Quvedo Carmona, Chris Sattler, Harry M. Steele, Vicente Talón, Ralph Thorsteinson, Winter & Findler, Leonid Yakutin, Aerospatiale, Alenis, Alstrom, Armada Española, Bazán, Daniel Bechenec, Blohm & Voss, Baoforos/Celsius, Celsius/Kockums, Centre IMP/Helio DCN Cherbourg, Clobrand Defence, DCN International, Denel LIW/Vektor, Eurosam, Finciatieri, GEC Alsthom, G.E.I.E. Eurotorp, GE Marine & Industrial Engines, Jeumont Industrie, Kollmorgen/GE, Konsberg, Litton Ingalls, Lockheed Martin, Marina Militare, Marine Nationale, Matra Bae Dynamics, McDonnell Douglas, Meval, Nordic Defence Industries A/S, Oerlikon-Contraves, Studio Grafico Restani, Royal Navy, STN Atlas Elektronik, Swedish Navy, Thomson Marconi, US Navy and Voith Hydro.

Documentalist: Albert Campanera i Rovira

Computing: José Manuel Rojo Ara and Albert Rojo Mateu

Production: Lema Editions S.L.
Editorial Director: Josep M. Parramón Homs
Text: Camil Busquets
Original Title: "Cazaminas, Patrulleros y Logísticos"
Co-ordination: Eduardo Hernández
Translation: Mike Roberts

© Lema Editions, S.L. 1999-05-12

ISBN 84-95323-14-1

Photosetting and photomechanics: Novasis, S.A.L.
Barcelona (Spain)
Printed in Spain

ARMAMENT AND TECHNOLOGY

MINEHUNTERS
PATROL BOATS
AND LOGISTICS

LEMA
Publications

Modern mine warfare has obliged navies all over the world to employ a very different kind of ship to what they are used to using. These ships are called minesweepers, a type of ship that remains something of a mystery to the general public.

The concept of minesweepers

The appearance of new types of underwater mines, triggered by multiple influence and computer controlled detonating devices, have obliged navies to find new methods of neutralizing them. This is because as the new devices became more sophisticated, new methods have to be worked out to render them harmless.

Traditional minesweeping, using dredges, was a slow and dangerous process that involved sailing one of those ships through suspected minefields. These ships towed acoustic and/or magnetic equipment, or cable cutters to cut the cables of moored mines, they supposedly 'swept' clean corridors through the area, though the reliability of the results was often questionable. There was always an element of risk, depending on the number and quality of ships that were used, and the time and

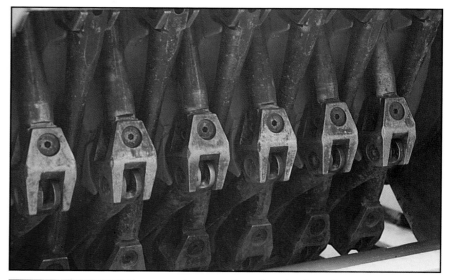

SQQ-14 MECHANISM

To minimise bearing errors that could be produced by a different VDS position to that of the actual ship. The 'fish' that operates with the VDS of the SQQ-14 sonar is lowered on the end of a specially articulated cable so that it move as little as possible when it goes down.

equipment that they had at their disposal.

Modern day minesweepers eliminate mines selectively. They detect them using very accurate sonar, which is positioned in the area by using highly sophisticated positioning techniques. Only when they are absolutely sure that they have discovered the whereabouts of a mine does the destruction process begin. A diver or a special remotely controlled vehicle, which is also equipped with television cameras, then places an explosive charge next to the device. When the diver and the vehicle are safe

MODERNISED SHIPS

The US Navy's Agile took part in the Korean and Vietnam Wars. They were modernised with VDS SQQ-14 sonar to keep them in operation. Once updated, some were transferred to other navies, such as the Spanish, in which they were supplied with ROV's and divers. In the photo is the Guadilquivir, M-43, the former Persistent, MSO-491.

the charge is then detonated and the mine should be destroyed.

The philosophy of the project

Owing to the special characteristics of both mines and minesweeping, ships designed for the purpose cannot have magnetic hulls and should not generate pressure waves on the seabed. They must have totally silent propulsion systems and should be able to maintain a steady course regardless of the condition of the sea. Safe and reliable systems for identifying mines, adequate electronic systems and effective mine-destroying equipment.

Therefore, the typical modern minesweeper is a ship with a GRP or wooden hull; special engines for transit and/or sweeping, and allows dynamic positioning to be maintained. Magnetic, acoustic and hydrostatic stealth, electronic positional sensors. The ship must also carry divers and their associated equip-

MINESWEEPER
The American Agile, Aggressive and Acme classes were built in large numbers (58 ships for the US Navy and 27 for allied countries) in the 1950s. They are entirely constructed from wood, their main engines are four Packard ID-1700 diesel engines in groups of two, each group working with a four-blade variable pitch propeller.

COMBINED CONSTRUCTION
The hull of the Tripartite is made entirely of GRP with balsa wood reinforcement in places, which is laminated into place and stratified with resin and textiles. The metal parts are directly attached to the wood by using metal supports that are built into the resin.

ment, together with hyperbaric chambers, and remotely operated vehicles.

Early minesweepers

During the Korean War, the USSR perfected a new kind of mine that was immune to the minesweeping technology of the time. The West's response was to build ships with aluminium frames and a double layer of mahogany planks. Specially demagnetised engines and detection equipment made up of active sonar that could detect mines on the sea bed was also installed. These ships were not yet considered minesweepers in the modern sense of the word, but as little by little they went on to incorporate more and more of the features of such vessels, they paved the way towards the class of ship that we know today.

Between 1953 and 1959, the Royal Navy built more than one hundred of the Ton class, a ship with a wooden hull and demagnetised engines. In 1973 the H.M.S. *Wilton* was commissioned, a modified Ton that was the first warship to be built using GRP. The same year several European navies, assisted by the US Navy, were involved in sweeping mines in the Suez Canal. An experience which undoubtedly influenced the philosophy behind a project for a new minesweeper, the MCMV (Mine Counter Measures Vessel).

In March of 1980, the Royal Navy received its first Hunt class minesweeper, the first of a series of ships built with GRP hulls. They were followed a few years later by the French-Belgian-Dutch Tripartite and the Italian Lerici. It is these ships on which the modern minesweeper has been based.

The Hunt Class

These ships came into service from 1980, the last one being completed in 1989. All were built by Vosper Thornycroft, two of them, the H.M.S. *Brecon* and the H.M.S. *Ledbury*, swept the waters around the Falkland Islands after the

HUNT MINESWEEPERS
These ships were the first minesweepers to be built and have a GRP hull. The idea of using these materials was so unusual that at first it was met with considerable reticence.

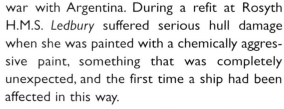
BELGIAN TRIPARTITES
Between 1985 and 1991 Belgium built ten Tripartite's, three of which were taken out of service in 1990 and were bought by France in 1997. In the photo, the Aster, the flagship, which is still in active service.

war with Argentina. During a refit at Rosyth H.M.S. *Ledbury* suffered serious hull damage when she was painted with a chemically aggressive paint, something that was completely unexpected, and the first time a ship had been affected in this way.

These ships displace 750 tons when fully loaded, measure 60 meters in length, 10 in breadth and have an average draught of 2.9 meters, and 3.4 meters at the propellers. For normal use they use two Deltic Ruston-Paxman 9-59K diesel engines, and Deltic Type 9-55B hydraulic engines when mine hunting and minesweeping, they are also fitted with a magnetic impulse generator. Their maximum speed is 15 knots when using the main engines and 8 knots when using hydraulic engines. In addition they are also fitted with bow and stern thrusters to aid positioning. They carry a crew of 45, six of whom are officers.

Their original minesweeping equipment was made up of combat divers and two French PAP 104 ROV (Remote Operated Vehicles) with mine sonar Type 193. For conventional towing, they had a Sperry Osborn Tag acoustic kit, for the magnetic variety they had MM Mk-II and Oropesa M Mk-3 mod. 2 for moored mines. All the minesweeping equipment was managed by

a CAAIS (Computer Aided Action Information System) that operated in conjunction with the dynamic positioning systems.

Its equipment and armaments were updated in the 1990s. The current weaponry is made up of a 30/75 mm DES/MSI DS 30 B gun (firing 650 rounds a minute), two 20-mm Oerlikon/BMARC GAM C-01 and two 12.7-mm machine guns.

The Tripartite

At the end of the 1970s, Belgium, France and Holland, all members of NATO and with common interests in the English Channel, agreed to the construction of a new class of minesweeper. For this reason, it was commonly known as the Tripartite, although the ten French ships were called Éridan class and the 15 Dutch ones were the Alkmaar class. Belgium built another 10 ships, but did not give them names, although the flagship of the series is called the Aster.

These ships all have normal GRP hulls, of uniform size. On the interior there are special stiffening frames and longitudinal girders so that the hull meets the required specification for resistance to explosions and seaworthiness. The interior of the hull is laminated with balsa wood to further reduce noise emissions.

GAETA MINESWEEPER
The eight ships of Gaeta class are essentially the same as the Lerici, but for a few minor differences such as the position of the mast, here shown in front of the funnel as opposed to on top of the bridge.

During sweeping operations, they can use a computerised control system, and they are equipped with ROV PAP 104, which was updated during the 1990s.

The Lerici

Between 1985 and 1996 Italy built 12 modern minesweepers in two rather different groups, four Lerici and eight Gaeta. These ships displace 620 and 697 tons respectively when fully loaded, are 50 and 50.2 meters in length, 9.9 wide and have a draught of 2.6 meters.

They have considerably different propulsion and dynamic positioning systems, based on a diesel engine with a variable speed propeller and three hydraulically powered active rudders, two at the stern and one at the bow. The diesel propulsion provides all of them with adequate thrust.

Their maximum speed is 14 knots, and 6 knots when minehunting; they have a range of 1,500 miles.

The crew of 47 is made up of four officers, seven divers and 36 ratings. The ships are fitted with a hyperbaric chamber, indispensable for easily and quickly dealing with the decompression problems that inevitably occur when a diver has to rise to the surface quickly.

They are also equipped with MIN 77 or Mk 2 and Italian Pluto ROV's; the former being used for depths below 65 meters. They also have VDS FIAR SQQ-14 (IT) high frequency sonar for detection and classification.

They are fitted with a single diesel engine with a variable speed propeller, two active rudders with electric motors and bow and stern thrusters for maneuvering and positioning. They have a maximum speed of 15 knots, and 7 knots when minesweeping. Their range is 3,000 miles at 12 knots.

CHARACTERISTIC SHAPES
Using GRP tends to result in rather a lot of straight edged shapes, at least on the gunwales and edges, because it is much more difficult to achieve curved shapes with this material than it is with steel or aluminium for example.

BUOYS AND BOATS

The Lerici are equipped with special buoys for marking the positions of mines, and also have rubber dinghies for operating with combat divers, behind which is the hyperbaric chamber.

HYPERBARIC CHAMBER

Practically all minesweepers that work with divers have a hyperbaric chamber in which divers can recover from 'bends', the name given to decompression sickness. They are usually for one person.

THE SWEEP DECK.

The sweep deck contains all of the towing and sweeping equipment. The yellow object is the ROV MIN fixed to a thwart. Up on the deck above there is a hyperbaric chamber. The crane is for launching the service boats and the MIN. The white objects are the equipment used for conventional mine-sweeping.

SHAPE OF THE STERN

The sterns of the Lerici have specially designed shapes for using two of their three active rudders. This way they can still maintain their position, no matter how rough the sea is.

ROV MIN

The MIN (Mine Neutralization Vehicle) is a miniature cable-controlled submarine. It is equipped with active sonar, an underwater TV camera, equipment for deepsea lighting, an ultrasonically controlled demolition charge and an articulated arm.

ENGINE CONTROL

These ships have a centralised system of engine control, this is situated next to the interior security control panel. However, during sweeping operations, the ship is generally controlled from the bridge, so as to minimise loss of life and damage should the ship set a mine off.

ACTIVE RUDDER CONTROL

The three active rudders are also controlled from this console, there is a similar control in the CIC. Basically, it is a console for controlling an active rudder (this can turn 360°, and has speed and directional control, there are usually two units at the stern and one at the bow.

HIGH MANEUVERABILITY

An active rudder is, basically, a propeller that is contained in a tube or a nozzle, which can turn 360 degrees. When the system is in use, these ships are extraordinarily maneuverable.

CIC

In the CIC (Combat Information Centre) are the controls for all of the sensors and the ROV. From here, the commander can control every movement and activity of the ship.

BRIDGE

The bridge of a Lerici is very different to that of a Tripartite. Here we can see the command console of the active rudders. During sweeping operations, the ship is controlled from the bridge and/or from the CIC.

The underwater mine, called a torpedo when it first appeared, is one of the most widely used and feared methods of naval warfare. They are unnerving, complex, difficult and expensive to neutralize. At the same time, they are capable of causing damage to the very ship that lays them.

Nowadays, the word "torpedo" refers to the self-propelled torpedo missile, whilst "mines" are stationary boms, although the most modern mines are sometimes able to release torpedos.

The underwater mine

Almost a century and a half has gone by since the American admiral, David Farragut, during the attack on the port of Mobile in the War of Succession, on the 5th of August, 1864, forgot all about mines and gave the order "damn the torpedoes, full speed ahead". After more than a century of development the underwater mine has become the most lethal danger of all, indiscriminate and extremely difficult for any ship to defeat.

Lethal weapon

The underwater mine was introduced to the world in the war between Japan and Russia in 1905. In that conflict, taking both sides into account, mines sank a total of four battleships, three cruisers, two coastal defense boats and two destroyers, while one battleship and six

MOTALA MINE
This Swedish patent mine dates back to 1930. It is a horn contact type mine with a lead anchor. The horns are made of lead and contain a small glass flask containing acid. On striking the ship, the acid spills out and closes a circuit to produce the explosion.

MECHANICAL CUTTERS
This mechanical cutter for cutting mine cables is armed before each operation. Once it has cut a cable, it has to be rearmed.

cruisers were seriously damaged.

In the First World War, just on the allied side alone, some 187,000 mines were laid at the approaches to the North Sea and close to the harbours by German submarines. The total number of ships lost to mines, on both sides, came to 23 battleships, 57 destroyers, 170 submarines and 497 merchant ships.

Amongst the merchant ships were several neutral vessels that had the misfortune to pass over mines, because mines, as is only too well known, do not make distinctions. They will sink whatever ship happens to be in its vicinity, whether it is a warship or a merchant ship, a friend or an enemy.

There are no exact statistics concerning the use and effects of mines in the Second World War. This was when the magnetic mine first appeared, an estimated total of somewhere between 15 and 20 million mines of all types

were built, although that does not necessarily mean that they were all used.

Later on, in the Korean War, the underwater mine was used by the North Koreans on different occasions and in different ports particularly Wonsan. This motivated the USA to build large quantities of minesweepers, such as the famous MSO and MSC class's with wooden hulls (Bluebird and Agile class), of which some are still in service today.

In Vietnam, the North Vietnamese also used mines, particularly in the port of Haiphong. The loss of time, the hold up of transit and immobilization of troops was, as a consequence, considerable.

In the war between Iran and Iraq, the

AMERICAN MINES

The USA uses several models of underwater mine for attacking submarines. Some of these include the CAPTOR Mk 60, which is dropped from aircraft (Mk 56), from submarines (Mk 57), mobiles (SLMM Mk 67), and torpedo based Mk 37 mod. 2 with a range of 16,000 meters, against surface vessels and is laid from submarines.

MCC-23 MINE

This mine was designed in France (Thomson/Sintra) and has a multiple influence detonator. It was specially designed for use on modern Daphné and Agosta class submarines.

Iranians used numerous mines that they had bought from Russia, many of which were of the moored type made in the Japan-Russia War. However, the fact is that a mine, as long as its circuits and detonator still work, is still a deadly weapon no matter how old it is, although modern methods for finding them makes it much easier to neutralize them. During that war the Libyan merchant ship Ghat laid mines throughout the Red Sea and the Gulf of Suez in the summer of 1984, causing serious damage to 18 ships, and the loss of the Barcelona, a 240,000 ton oil tanker.

In the Desert Storm and Desert Shield operations, the US Navy noted three incidents involving mines. One of these was when the air-

craft carrier U.S.S. *Tripoli* was left with an 8 m2 hole In the starboard bow, beneath its waterline, which put her out of action for a long time while repairs were carried out. Another incident was when the AEGIS cruiser U.S.S. *Princeton* was seriously damaged by what appears to have been a pair of Italian Manta type mines. The third incident involved the Oliver Hazard Perry class frigate U.S.S. *Samuel B. Roberts*, which suffered some damage but remained operational. The cost of repairing the three ships came to 125 million dollars, substantially more than the Iraqi investment of less than $30,000. And that is without taking into account the inconvenience caused while the ships were being repaired, and the psychological effects on the crews. The threat of mines is one of the situations that causes the most stress amongst crews, and is a reflection impotence that most navies have against them.

Types of mine

The most traditional mine is the so-called moored mine, which is fixed to the seabed by an anchored cable and stays in the water at a predetermined depth. There are several types: those with contact horns, those that work by the increase in water pressure as a vessel passes over it, etc. This type of mine is normally laid from ships and boats fitted with mine rails on the deck.

In the Second World War, the magnetic mine made its first appearance, which is laid from airplanes or submarines. It caused many

GMI 100 ROCKAN MINE
This modern Swedish mine has a multiple influence detonator. It weighs 190 kg and is about 1 meter long, 0.8 m wide and 0.3 high. It was specially designed to protect against invasion, meaning that it is a defensive measure that makes it very difficult to land invading forces on the purchasing country's coast.

EMC II MINE
This German antenna mine was used extensively before and during the Second World War, and was also used by the Spanish Navy. This photo shows the shape of its explosive float, together with the equipment for laying this mine.

British losses during the first months of the war, until one was found that could be disarmed and examined. This resulted in countermeasures being developed against it.

A huge amount of technological advances came as a result of that war, and the magnetic mine was only one type to be introduced, others included the TDD (Target Detection Devices), which were subsequently fitted to other types of mines. The acoustic mine appeared soon after, followed by the pressure mine, and they were used extensively up until the invention of the intelligent, or computerised mine.

This type of mine is similar to many of those mentioned above, the difference is that the detonator incorporates a microprocessor, which is able to differentiate between ships, even temporarily deactivating itself and 'hiding' on the seabed, and thus evading sweeping

attempts. There are even mines that are immune to the *pings* of echo searchers, which makes these mines extremely potent and dangerous weapons.

Also worthy of mention are mobile mines, something like a self-propelled torpedo. Half buried on the seabed, they only switch on when their sensor picks up a certain signal, whereupon they direct themselves towards their target.

The worst thing of all about modern mine warfare is that, owing to their low price, mines of very little complexity are within reach not only of any country, but also any sophisticated terrorist or smuggler.

Minesweeping

The sweeping of a minefield is a highly complex and dangerous operation. Though preference can be given to either speed or safety, a balance has to be reached between the two.

If speed is the main priority, the MCMV will be exposed to the possibility of a mine exploding, and the loss of the ship. However, opting for safety can mean that the operation will take too long to clear the minefield. If this is the case, then a balance has to be chosen between the two according to a pre-

MCC-23 MINE

Spanish submarines, designed in France, use the same MCC mine, though like the submarines they are actually manufactured in Spain. The EESA Company (Equipos Electrónicos, S.A.) manufactured these mines, that can work at depths up to 150 meters.

MOORED MINES

This illustration shows the different parts of the equipment that is towed for immobilizing moored mines. On the right are the cutters that break the anchoring cables.

determined percentage, which should never be higher than 90%.

Transit channels

The sweeping of a complete minefield is a task that can take up to months of patient and dangerous work, therefore the usual solution is just to clear one corridor through the area. This channel is marked with buoys, and provided that ships keep within them, their safety is assured.

Each minesweeper tows along a detector, and the channel is not declared free until each different one has passed through the zone. The width of the channel varies depending on the

types of detectors and sweeping methods, and it is not unusual for more than one ship to be used so as to make the channel wider. A normal width for a corridor cleared of moored mines would be about 200 or 230 meters.

Minesweeping methods

The most common method is that for moored mines. This involves passing through mine infested waters towing a long cable that has one or more cutters attached that cut the cables that moors the mines. When cut, the mine floats to the surface and gunfire is used to make it explode at a safe distance.

Magnetic mines are immobilized by exposing them to strong magnetic fields. This can either be done from the air (using an airplane or helicopter) or by special ships equipped with coils that produce the required magnetic field which explodes the mine at a safe distance from the ship.

VICKERS H-5 MINE

Antenna mines do not need the ship to hit its float or the body of the mine, but just to touch its antenna that is kept tense by the upper float. In this cross-section of a Vickers H-5 mine, you can see the red cylinder inside, which contains the explosive charge. The upper float, coloured red, holds the antenna, and the green pieces are used for dropping the mine into place.

CARBONIT MINE

Submarines are able to lay moored mines with hydrostatic mechanisms. The explosive float rises until the mechanism holds it in place, and should not be confused with hydrostatic detonators. This illustration shows the German Carbonit mine, built for Turkey between 1914 and 1915, and widely used in the First World War.

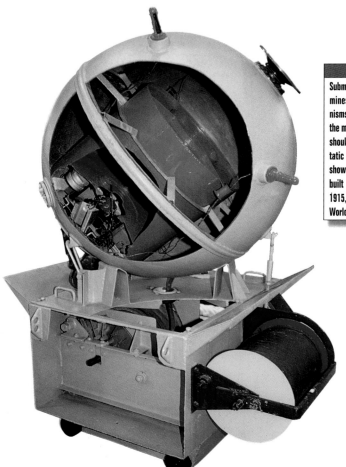

Those with acoustic detonators are dealt with similarly, a sound generator can cause the mines to explode. Hydrostatic pressure mines, however, are more difficult to deal with, because the pressure wave that a hull produces is not so easy to imitate.

However, the use of multiple detonators, which are designed to react to only certain influences or signatures, complicates the matter further, because they are capable of ignoring any one of the traditional methods of immobilizing mines.

The consequence of all this has been the minesweeper, a ship that detects and neutralizes mines one by one, but minesweeping technology has to keep pace with the development of the mines themselves, in an on going struggle between one technology and another.

t is not easy to say when minesweepers first appeared in the true sense of the word. A minesweeper is, strictly speaking, a ship that locates mines selectively, one after the other. It is unclear as to whether a ship that simply tows along a heavy dredge in the traditional way can also be considered a minesweeper.

Following from experiences with the Hunt, Tripartite and Lerici, new ships have been developed, in many cases they are updated versions of previous designs rather than new designs in their own right. However, that is not to say that all the newer ships are mere updates of their predecessors.

The Malaysian Mahumiru, Indonesian Pulau Rengat and German Lindau classes are examples of modified vessels. More revolutionary are the Australian Bay and the Norwegian Oksoy class. Newly designed ships that use tried and tested methods include the American Avenger and Osprey, the British-Spanish Sandown/Segura and German Lindau/Troika and Frankenthal.

INDONESIAN TRIPARTITE

The two Pulau class ships are fitted with MTU 12V 396 TC382 diesel engines and a single variable pitch propeller. When sweeping, they use a retractable Schottle propulsion unit and two bow thrusters. Electrical power is produced by three groups of turbo-generators with Turbomeca gas turbines.

Born from the Hurt, Tripartite and Lerici
Mahamiru

The Italian Intermarine Company, in Sarzana, designed and constructed the Lerici/Gaeta class that have been successfully exported, though, they would have sold a great many more if their export policy had been more flexible.

The first foreign country to purchase one of the Lerici class was Malaysia in 1985, this

THE LERICI

Malaysia has four Lerici class minesweepers: *Mahamiru*, *Jerai* (in the photo), *Ledang* and *Kinabalu*, two based in Lumut and the other two in Labuan. They can stay up to 14 days at sea. They now include tactical data systems.

was followed by a further four which had been ordered on the 20th of February, 1981. They used a somewhat modified system of propulsion, which instead of a single main engine and propeller they were fitted with two MTU 12V 396 TC82 engines and variable pitch Ka-Me-Wa propellers. They can stay at sea for as long as two weeks. However, they kept the three Isotta Fraschini ID 36 SS 6V engines to power the two Riva Calzoni hydrojets that are used when sweeping, and are activated by a hydraulic system. The sweeping equipment consists of Thomson Sintra TSM 2022 sonar with a 2060 HF monitor, and a Thomson-CSF IBIS II minesweeping system with two updated PAP-104 ROVs. They also have an Oropesa O MIS-4 dredge.

Another country that possesses the Lerici is Nigeria, who received two very similar ships to the Malaysian ones in 1987 and 1998, though these had Pluto ROVs instead of PAP.

Australia is currently building a group of six

LINDAU MINESWEEPERS

In the Lindau class, although the ships were originally meant to be identical, there are two very differently used types. This photo shows a 331, the *Minden*.

systems to the original ships, namely MTU 12V 396 TC382 diesel engines with a single variable pitch propeller. When carrying out minesweeping operations, a Schottle propulsion unit and two bow thrusters are employed.

Lindau and Lindau/Troika

The lead ship was the first warship to be built in Germany since the Second World War, and was launched on the 16th of February 1957. All the technology of the time was incorporated into the ships. They were built entirely of wood, using the double diagonal system. Eighteen ships were completed, and were later modernized during the 1970s. The original plan was for a series of identical vessels, but there are in fact two vwry different designs. Only 11 are still in service (five 331 Type minesweepers and six 351 Type or Troika guides. They use Plessey 193 M high frequency sonar (100-300 MHz) and ECA/PAP-104 ROVs.

The most revolutionary minesweepers
The Bay

Australia designed the H.M.A.S. *Rushcutter* and H.M.A.S. *Shoalwater* at the beginning of the 1980s though the two ships were not accepted by the RAN until June 1994, seven and eight years after their respective completion. They are catamarans, constructed from GRP, with three meter wide hulls and they displace 178 tons. If we take into account their dimensions (30.9 meters long, 9m wide and 2 meters of draught), you will notice that they have relatively small displacements however, it is said that

Huon (the last should be ready in 2002), although this appears to be an Italian-Australian *joint venture*. This seems to suggest that Italy has abandoned its policy of demanding that all these ships be built in Italy.

Pulau Rengat

These are two Dutch built Tripartite minesweepers. Twelve should have built altogether, with ten of them being built in Indonesia; but the program had to be abandoned for financial reasons. They used very different propulsion

BAY CATAMARANS

France first attempted the use of catamarans for minesweeping, with its failed BAMO (Bâtiment Anti Mines Oceanique) project. They have the advantage of being very stable and maneuverable ships, although they do suffer from the inconvenience of having to carry most of the equipment in interchangeable containers and their range is limited.

they are excellent vessels, and their features have been highly praised. In particular, positioning the engines on the upper deck, keeping their noise well away from the water, has substantially reduced their acoustic signature.

The Oksoy

Ten years after the failure of American technology with its disastrous MSH Cardinal class, Norway perfected its Oksoy class, the first Surface Effect Ship to be mass-produced. Of the nine ships, only four carry the kind of equipment that makes them true minesweepers. They are sandwich built with FRP (Fibre Reinforced Plastic), with two MTU 12V 396 TE 84 main engines, and Kverner Eureka hydrojets; another two 8V 396 TE54 engines operate the buoyancy ventilators. They have Thomson Sintra/Simrad TSM 2023N sonar with two Pluto ROV.

An old system for new ships
The Avenger

These 14 ships were the first MCM to be built by the USA in 25 years. They are built of wood with an exterior GRP coating. The deck has been constructed similarly.

There is nothing new about the propulsion

HYDRAULIC PROPULSION
The Osprey, like most minesweepers, these vessels have two engines, although in this case it is somewhat different, as it has been fitted with 180 hp hydraulic engines on its VS epicycloid propellers.

system, using four diesel engines connected in pairs to each propeller, and they also have low speed engines for use when sweeping. Electrical power is generated by gas turbines. They use AQQ-30 sonar (an updated version of AQQ-14) although, owing to certain problems, on the MCM-1, 10 and 14 it was replaced by SQQ-32. They make use of an SLQ-48 MNS ROV.

The *Avenger* participated in the Desert Storm and Desert Shield operations and returned to the USA in 1991 under her own power

(she had been transported to the Gulf on board the Dutch heavy lift ship *Super Servant 3*). On this ocean voyage, it was able to show off its excellent sailing capabilities.

The Osprey

After the embarrassing failure of the SES Cardinal, a prototype that did not pass an extensive testing procedure because its GRP hull came apart when struck by shock waves, together with the fuel supply problems that the Italian Isotta Fraschini engines presented, the USA went into negotiation with Intermarine for the construction of a modified Lerici.

Intermarine USA took charge of most of the construction at Savannah (Georgia), but Avondale Industries in New Orleans (Louisiana) took charge of the 3rd to 7th ships. These were the first GRP ships to appear in the US Navy, built with a single hull, without interior reinforcements, with the frames and decks being installed afterwards.

The propulsion equipment, with VS epicycloids being driven by Isotta Fraschini ID 36 SS 6V-AM engines, both propel and position the ship, although there is also a bow thruster. The sonar and ROV are identical to those of the Avenger, the SSQ-32 and the MNS.

The Sandown

The British Sandown class SRMH (Single

THE FRANKENTHAL

They are built with demagnetised steel, not unlike that used for submarines. Which makes them rather unusual for a modern minesweeper in that they do not use GRP. They displace 650 tons when fully loaded, and are 54.5 m long, 9.2 m wide and their draught is of 2.6 m. When on passage between ports or areas they use their two diesel engines, this is augmented by another propeller powered by an electric motor when they are on sweeping operations.

Role Mine Hunter) were designed by Vosper-Thornycroft and entered service from 1989. A total of 12 ships were ordered, and eight are already operating, with two on the point of joining them and a further two expected in 2001. They are specially designed for seeking mines in coastal areas and in the open sea, though not out in deep water. They are propelled by Voith Schneider epicycloids powered by diesel engines when on passage and electrical ones when they are sweeping. They have Marconi Type 2093 sonar and a PAP-104 Mk 5 ROV.

The Al Jawf

Saudi Arabia ordered two Sandown 'hand keys' that were presented in 1991, 1993 and 1996, although the first ship did not set off for that country until 1995, followed by the other two in 1996 and 1997. A further three ships have already been named, but have not been contracted. They are slightly different to the British originals.

The Segura

When Spain decided to substitute their four Guadalete/Agile they had Tripartite, Lerici

and Sandown minesweepers in mind. The Troika option, which had originally been discussed, was eventually discarded. Of the three remaining options, the Tripartite was considered too expensive, and certain industrial inconveniences did away with the Lerici idea.

Therefore, the Sandown was selected; a ship that could also be marketed to third party

SPEED AND AUTONOMY

The Sandown class has a maximum speed of 13 knots using their diesel engines and 6.5 knots when sweeping and using their electric motors. They have a maximum range of 3,000 miles at 12 knots. The whole crew can live on board (34 men, 5 officers) and they also have additional accommodation for a further six crew.

countries, provided the corresponding project rights could be acquired. E.N.Bazán took sole charge of the construction, without using any foreign partners.

The resulting CME (Caza Minas Español/Spanish Minesweeper) is, as would be expected, very similar to the Sandown, being particularly similar to the British vessel with regards to the FGRP (FibreGlass Reinforced Plastic) technology that they use.

The CME has avoided building a thick single hull with interior reinforcements. It gets around the problem of easily broken lines and edges by using an adequately flexible system that stops the hull from breaking or coming apart, which is capable of absorbing the bulges and deformations caused by explosions.

At the same time, it tries not to make interior reinforcements with balsa wood or synthetic foams and relies on the resistance of the flexible resin joints, thus obtaining thicker and sturdier hulls.

The propulsion operates with VS epicycloids, with two additional bow turbines. It has Raytheon/ENOSA SQQ-32 sonar and a Pluto Plus ROV.

NORWEGIAN SES

The Oksoy is a Surface Effect Ship that is supported on a cushion of air between the two hulls. and two stern to bow flexible membranes. With this system, the draught which when stopped is 2.5 meters, is reduced to 0.84 when underway.

A minefield does not just include magnetic mines, usually there is a mixture of different types. Therefore, a wide variety of sweeps are still needed.

Minesweeping

Minesweepers seek and eliminate mines one by one, although once the bearings of each mine has been discovered and plotted, they can destroy more than one at the same time. They are also assisted by ships that work 'blindly', with a special type of sweep that it tows along. When the ship enters the minefield this will either explode the mine or cut the mooring cable so that the mine will rise to the surface were it can be destroyed by gunfire.

There are also ships that can serve the two functions at once, they tow light sweeps, which are normally for use against moored mines. Although, depending on time and conditions, special ships may be needed to tow heavier dredges.

There is another option, currently very popular, that involves the passing of a Remote Operated Vehicle (ROV) through the minefield, and mines can be seen via a closed circuit TV

SLQ-48 MNS

This is the ROV used on American MCMV. It is controlled by a 1,500-meter umbilical chord, which transmits power, command, video signals and sonar. It reaches speeds up to 6 knots. It weighs 1,247 kg, is 3.8 m long, and 0.9 m high and wide. At the bow, it has pincers that it can use to cut the cables of moored mines and it can deposit an explosive charge onto bottom mines.

system and it can detonate mines at will. However, the machine can easily be lost in the process, which is why using this method is often met with reticence, because a minefield can contain dozens of mines, even hundreds, and there is usually only one (and two or three at the very most) ROV per ship. It is so much cheaper to fire a few rounds of low calibre bullets at the mine to destroy it, than it is to loose the ROV.

These ships are faced with such dangers, and the crew undergoes such stressful work, that these ships were once said to be crewed by "men of steel on ships of wood".

Modern minesweepers

No self-respecting navy, no matter how small and unimportant it may be, should be without some kind of ship adapted for the destruction of mines. For this reason, it is quite normal for any suitable vessel to be adapted for the purpose, even fishing trawlers have been used, a cheap solution to the problem of so many losses.

If we take all the naval forces of the world into account there must be about 620 ocean, coastal, river, light and heavy vessels that are used for such work, including many that are not exclusively minesweepers. According to the most recent records, 160 countries have their own navy, which would make an average of nearly four vessels per country, which would rise to more than six or seven if all the MCMVs were taken into account.

Of all the existing classes, perhaps the most interesting are the Canadian Kingston, the Russian Sonya and the German Hameln. Here we shall also examine the Indian Pondicherry class and the Indonesian Pulau Rote class.

The Kingston

These twelve ships were built by Halifax Shipyards between 1996 and 1999. They can be used as limited minesweepers or patrol boats, and have Oropesa SLQ-38 sweeps (also for

SWEEPING MINES
These ships carry out patient, silent and undervalued work, in which the crew put their lives at greater risk than on any other ship. In the photo, two Estonian vessels are shown in operation.

PAP PLUS
The total number of PAP is nearly 350, and 14 different navies use them. They have carried out over 30,000 combat missions in locations like the Red Sea, Falkland Islands, Persian Gulf and the Gulf War.

deep-sea use), ROV Sutec, towed MacDonald Dettwiler sonar and container space for equipment as and when required. They are well designed for divers and for minesweeping equipment. They are officially called MCDV (Marine Coast Defence Vessel).

These ships use diesel/electric propulsion, this consists two Jeumont CI 560 L engines and another two Lips which are powered by four Wärtsila UD 23V12 diesel engines fitted with Jeumont ANR-53-50 generators. They travel at speeds of 15 knots when on passage, and have a range of 5,000 miles at 12 knots. When towing sweeps they can reach 10 knots.

They have a crew of 37 men for minesweeping and 31 for patrol, a large proportion of which are reservists.

The Sonya

Russia has different kinds of vessels, amongst which the 1265 class stands out. There are several versions, two for internal use (0 and A) and another, E, for export. They were built in two cities, Saint Petesburg in the west and Vladivostok in the east, beginning in 1973 and the last one was completed in 1995. 39 of the ships are used by the Russian marines. Several units have been sold to Bulgaria (4), Cuba (5), Ethiopia (1), Ukraine (3) and Vietnam (4). They have a wooden hull with a plastic coated exterior.

They have all the usual equipment, such as MG 69/79 sonar, but also have other less common features for a boat of this type, such as IFF,

two CIWS AK-630 guns and even twin quadruple mounts for SAM SA-N-5 Grail. They can also function as mine layers, with eight mines per ship.

The Hameln

These ships have very similar hulls to the Frankenthal minesweeper, and their displacements are also comparable (635 as opposed to 650 tons and 54.4 x 9.2 x 2.5 against 54.5 x 9.2 x 2.6). Both classes are constructed out of demagnetised steel at the same yards (Kröger-

werft, Lüssenwerft and Abeking & Rasmussen).

The ten units were completed between 1989 and 1991. They were the first German Mine Warfare (MIW) ships to be classed as Schnelles Minensuchboot (Rapid Minesweeper) as opposed the older classification of Schnelles Minenkampfboot (Rapid Mine Warfare Ship). They have two MTU 16V 538 TB91 diesel engines with twin variable pitch propellers than can drive the vessel up to speeds of 18 knots.

As with Russian Sonya, they carry mines, this time 60, and have auxiliary missile weapons (two quadruple SAM Stinger launchers) and two 40/70-mm guns. They have DSQS-11 M Atlas Elektronik high frequency hull sonar.

Five ships will be converted into supply ships for the Troika, for which their mechanical SDG-31 minesweeping equipment will be improved. The other five will probably be converted into normal minesweepers.

The Pondicherry

Between 1978 and 1989, India received a dozen ocean going mine warfare vessels with steel hulls. These differed from the Russian originals, the Natya, in that they did not have ramps at the stern. They have GKT-2 sweeps

M 1096

tical stages of the minesweeping process.

Surface ROV

The great danger and difficulty that modern mine clearance faced led to the need for new solutions that would prevent the loss of ships and casualties amongst the crew. During the Second World War, Germany pioneered the use of several remote control machines (Mistel aeroplane, Henschel HS-293 flying bombs, Goliath tanks, etc.) in an attempt to minimize their own casualties while at the same time inflict maximum damage to the Allies. These eventually led to the appearance of small, and sometimes not so small, surface vessels, while at the same time retaining the features of a traditional minesweeper.

Underwater ROV

At the same time, the increasing use of robots in industry brought about the concept of autonomous cable controlled vehicles. They quickly gained popularity for being reliable and economical because they could be mass-produced. This popularity increased when they were fitted with small lightweight high-resolution TV cameras. This allowed a contact to be visually inspected, on a monitor on board the ship, from a safe distance.

for moored mines, AT-2 for acoustic ones and TEM-3 for magnetic ones. They displace 804 tons and use two type 504 diesel engines with variable pitch propellers that allow the ships to travel at up to sixteen knots.

They can also be used for laying mines (with a capacity for up to 10 mines). One of the twelve has been prepared as an AGI for the acquisition of information (an intelligent or spy ship), and the flagship was once used as a presidential yacht, for which it was painted white.

Pulau Rote

Indonesia gave a new look to its fleet in 1993 when it acquired a number of ships from the German government, which at the time was getting rid of most of those that had belonged to the old German Democratic Republic.

Amongst the 40 ships were nine Kondor II, whose original role were as minesweepers, but with the reunification of Germany they became surplus to requirements.

ROV

So called Remote Operated Vehicles, and each of the succesive innovations and modifications, such as simple explosive charges and intelligent munition, were inspired by the need to minimise human losses during the most cri-

THE PONDICHERRY

The Indian Navy has a dozen of these ships, all built in Russia at the Isora shipyard in Saint Petersburg. They displace 804 tons and are 61 meters long. They have two Type 504 diesel engines and variable pitch propellers. Their maximum speed is 16 knots.

SEEHUND SURFACE ROV

The Bundesmarine has 18 of these radio-controlled boats, which have acoustic and magnetic minesweeping equipment.

Disposable ROV

A new possibility has recently been discussed, one that has been given very little thought in the past; the use of disposable ROV that are lost along with the explosion of the mine. It is difficult to say at present if the proposal will ever be used on a wide scale, but it is an idea that is being seriously considered, with most reservations centered around the high cost.

Since the 1980s, technology has come up with several types and models of ROV for mine clearance and other underwater operations. It is worth remembering that the detection, identification and classification of a mine, is a practically identical process to that of any other underwater project; such as explorations of the Titanic and other shipwrecks, the study of deep sea oil drilling and gas pipelines and the laying of foundations for a bridge. Even methods for seeking drowned people are almost identical.

Clear proof of the value of such technology can be seen by looking back over combat events that have occurred over the last decade, particularly the Desert Storm and Desert

DOUBLE EAGLE MK-2

This Swedish ROV made by Bofors belongs to the generation of all-purpose vehicles. It is also appropriate for industrial use, although there are versions that can be adapted for military uses. They have two propellers at the stern, with lateral and vertical propellers for sideways and vertical/downward movement. This picture shows a SUTEC Double Eagle Mk-2 with frontal sonar.

Shield operations, in which ROV of different types deactivated or destroyed some 3,000 mines.

THE KINGSTON

The RCN has twelve Kingston class minesweepers, six for work on the Pacific coast and six for the Atlantic, particularly in the Gulf of St. Lawrence, with a base in Quebec.

The appearance of new materials and propellers, together with more powerful engines and computerised systems, has allowed technical development to advance to the stage that the equipment we regard as being standard today, was in the realms of science fiction only a few decades ago.

ANT

Advanced Naval Technologies, often referred to by the acronym ANT, refers to a series of ships with unusual features and characteristics which have gradually been introduced to both the military and civilian naval worlds.

In the diagram that appears on page 27, each of the different acronyms, names and types of ships are detailed, along with the buoyancy systems they use; together with other vessels they can be considered hybrids and/or combinations.

Resistance versus speed

Hydrostatic buoyancy is based on Archimedes principle, which is the basis on which all forms of waterborne craft are able to float. The power that a ship generates to move

ASR-21, PIGEON

The Pigeon and Ortolan were built after the loss of the *Thresher*, SSN 593, in 1963, with the aim of providing the fleet with ASR/DSRV, which was able to rescue the crews from submarines in deep water.

CONTROL PANEL

Despite being more technologically complex, the control panel of an SES is no different to that of a conventional ship or an ACV. The photograph shows the *SES-16*.

forward is mainly absorbed by two major forces. A) Friction as the hull passes through the water and B) the resistance of waves and the hulls own wake. The former increases in relation to the speed of the craft. The latter, however, does so in proportion to its quinta potencia. If a ship has a hull with traditional shape, there are physical limitations to the speed it can reach no matter how much power is used to propel the hull.

ANT is an attempt to find new solutions to the problem, with completely new concepts in ship design, be they related to safety,

stability, speed, military capabilities, or a combination of all these factors.

These ships have been made possible by new technology and innovative propulsion systems; lighter and higher powered engines, highly resistant and reliable synthetic materials and so on. However, the most important factor has been computerization, which has greatly assisted in the carrying out of complex and extensive investigation and research.

Main types of buoyancy

Of all the types of buoyancy that appear in the diagram, the most used by navies are SES, catamarans, hydrofoils, SWATH and ACV.

Depending on its characteristics, the buoyancy of a ship can be divided into hydrostatic (the Archimedes Principle), hydrodynamic (gliding), and aerodynamic.

- Hydrostatic buoyancy: the weight of the volume of water displaced is equal to that of the ship.

- Hydrodynamic buoyancy: the weight of the water displaced by the ship above certain speeds is less than that of the ship. The difference is produced by dynamic thrust.

VICTORIOUS SWATH CLASS

This type of ship is most widely used in the USA and Japan (Victorious and Impeccable class, 4+1, and Hibiki, 2). The USA uses them on T-AGOS missions or for ocean surveillance, using SOSUS (SOund SUrveillance System), because the waters of the North Atlantic, where they patrol to track the movements of Russian SSBN and SSN, can be extremely hazardous, especially in winter.

HYDROJET PROPULSION

These ships tend to have twin propulsion systems, known as *hullborne* and *foilborne*. The former are for cruising, usually with diesel engines and a retractable propeller, in hydrostatic conditions. When the foils are unfolded (hydrodynamic buoyancy), the same happens, but the hydrojets are powered by gas turbines.

- Aerodynamic buoyancy: the weight of the water displaced by the hull above certain speeds if the hull is shaped in a particular way, is less than that of the ship. The difference is produced by the buoyancy created by the hull shape.

Aerostatic buoyancy: the weight of the water displaced by the ship is, regardless of the speed that is reached, less than that of the ship.

SES

This could be the ship of most interest in the future. It is, basically, a catamaran with flexible flaps between the two hulls, one is at the stern and the other at the bow. When they are deployed between the hulls they form an enclosed cavity. Air is injected into this cavity at low pressure, causing an effective reduction of the draught, and therefore, displacement.

Its main attributes are: a large amount of equipment can be carried, a usefully large platform surface, high speed, good performance at sea, excellent maneuverability, high reliability and low vulnerability. Amongst its main features include a complex structure, a new type of propulsion, light construction, control

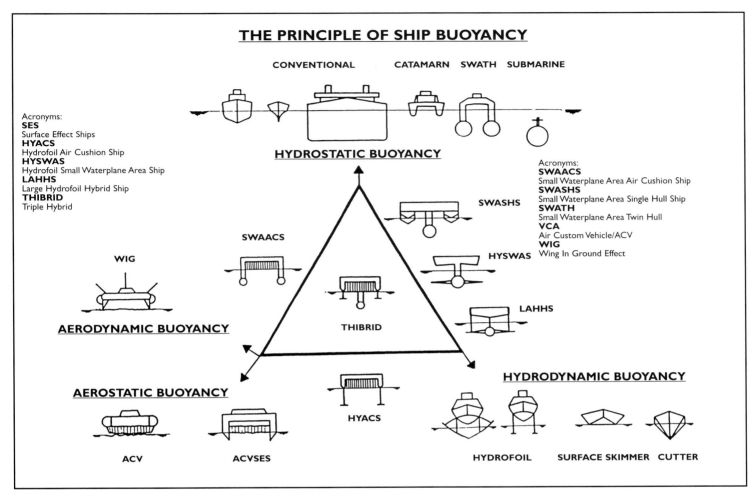

THE PRINCIPLE OF SHIP BUOYANCY

CONVENTIONAL   CATAMARN   SWATH   SUBMARINE

Acronyms:
SES
Surface Effect Ships
HYACS
Hydrofoil Air Cushion Ship
HYSWAS
Hydrofoil Small Waterplane Area Ship
LAHHS
Large Hydrofoil Hybrid Ship
THIBRID
Triple Hybrid

Acronyms:
SWAACS
Small Waterplane Area Air Cushion Ship
SWASHS
Small Waterplane Area Single Hull Ship
SWATH
Small Waterplane Area Twin Hull
VCA
Air Custom Vehicle/ACV
WIG
Wing In Ground Effect

HYDROSTATIC BUOYANCY

SWASHS

SWAACS

WIG

HYSWAS

AERODYNAMIC BUOYANCY

LAHHS

THIBRID

AEROSTATIC BUOYANCY

HYDRODYNAMIC BUOYANCY

HYACS

ACV   ACVSES

HYDROFOIL   SURFACE SKIMMER   CUTTER

---

of thrust and an extensive R&D program. Its military field of duty: low capacity frigates and corvettes, minesweepers, patrol boats and special purpose ships. These ships tend operate better with hydrojet propulsion systems.

Catamarans

The catamaran takes full advantage of the excellent buoyancy obtained by the wide gap between the two hulls. At the same time, this space allows it to have a wide and unobstructed deck, along with an excellent maneuverability due to the distance between the propellers and the rudders on each hull. This also assists with the maintenance of momentum.

It is extremely stable and the fact that outside forces do not affect its displacement adds to this security. Its very configuration gives it unique sailing qualities, which have been perfected over a number of years. The USA made use of two large catamarans called the Pigeon and Ortolan but in the nineties both were taken out of service and never replaced. These

BUOYANCY OF SHIPS

This diagram shows the main types of ANTS (Advanced Naval Technology Ships), classified according to their buoyancy types. As can be seen, many of the hybrids have not been developed much further than the initial stages of investigation.

two ships were originally created as replacements for the thresher, which was lost in 1963, for rescuing deeply stranded submarine crews. Australia, meanwhile, still uses two Bay class Catamarans for minesweeping called Shoalwater and Rushcutter. They have formed a part of the RAN since june 1994.

Hydrofoils

The hydrofoil is a surface skimming boat with a planing hull, to which supports for foils are attached (these are similar to aircraft wings). When the boat picks up speed, and the angles of the foils are changed in relation to the position of the boat, the main hull is lifted out of the water and the boat rides on the foils as it moves forward through the water.

Engines and propellers are usually positioned in the main hull, but on these boats they are generally placed at the end of a long shaft or are encased at the end of the supports. Although in principle they only use propellers, more modern versions also have hydrojets, in which case they are known as *jetfoils*. They can reach high speeds of around 50 knots, but can be somewhat precarious to operate, particularly on heavy seas.

The oldest and most famous hydrofoils are the BTNA, which were used at the beginning of the 20th Century in Italy (1906-1908) and America (1919). The German Kriegsmarine used the TS-1 class in 1941 and 1942. The improved prototype, TS-6, fell into Russian hands at the end of the Second World War, and was studied and tested on the Volga.

From the 1960s onwards they have been used in the navies of the USA, Italy, Israel and the USSR. Nowadays, very few are still in service although one notable exception is the Italian manufactured Spaviero, of which sis were made in the early eighties. A decade later, Japan received the license to manufacture three more vessels, entering service from 1993 to 1995.

SWATH

These ships are usually the ones that can be expected to reach the greatest speeds. Several civilian versions are being used today (as ferries, cruisers and so on), and there has even been talk of building them large enough to be able to operate aircraft.

Although at first glance they may look like

HYDROJET PROPULSION
Hydrojet propulsion is a regular feature of SES, being an ideal system for this kind of ship. The photograph shows a view of the stern of the *SES-16* with its Castoldi hydrojets.

LARGE CATAMARANS
The US Navy used large catamarans between 1973 and 1992. It had two USS: *Pigeon*, ASR-21 and *Ortolan*, ASR-22. They were taken out of service in 1992 and 1995 respectively.

catamarans, that could not be further from the truth, although they do use a similar form of hydrostatic buoyancy. The SWATH design features a superstructure on struts above two completely submerged hulls with a large fin on the upper section. The hulls are joined by a common structure above the water.

In principle, this vessel offers the same advantages as the catamaran, but with one additional bonus. The fact that the two hulls are submerged several metres beneath the surface of the water makes this boat particularly good to handle, because the effects of the waves are considerably reduced under the

cooled by water, they are therefore the ideal solution.

For all these reasons, they are considered ideal passenger ships (the low amount of movement greatly reduces seasickness) and aircraft carriers (because of the stable platform), and special boats. The low ratio between length and breadth, around three or four to one, allows for the construction of large and high superstructures, and by using a modular concept more efficient use of the interior space and lower costs can be achieved. Japan and the USA are the main users of SWATH ships, of which the Victorious, Impecable and Hibiki are probably the most outstanding. Many of the American vessels are needed for ocean surveillance in the cold and precarious waters of the North Atlantic.

water. Therefore, these ships have better 'sea keeping' than any other seagoing vessel of this type.

The larger space between the two hulls, which makes these ships exceptionally wide, and the possibility of adding one or more decks to the structure that joins them, mean that these ships can have much larger superstructures. The stability of these vessels at sea, which can carry surprisingly large amounts and are extremely comfortable to travel on, makes them ideal passenger boats.

Moreover, their configuration allows them to reach high speeds without many of the problems a single hull would produce, because the two narrow supports, the only parts that cut the water, offer little resistance and form a low degree of wake, meaning that high speeds can be reached on much less power than would otherwise be necessary.

The critical factor concerning these boats is the propulsion system that, for construction reasons, is more convenient if it can be placed inside the two hull bodies. This generally implies the use of electric engines, because they are not so mechanically complex as diesel engines and do not need any form of exhaust system. They do, though, need an adequate cooling system instead. However, with the high effectiveness of cryogenics, and permanent magnet electric motors (an electric motor without brushes), which are easily

MINESWEEPERT CATAMARANS

The Royal Australian Navy has two minesweeper-catamarans, the Bay class *Shoalwater* and *Rushcutter*. Both came into service in 1986 and 1987, although they were not accepted by the RAN until June 1994.

SPARVIERO HYDRFOILS

Italy built six Sparviero between 1980 and 1984 (the photo shows the *Griffone*), P-424, similar to the Pegasus. The manufacturing license for three units was given to Japan (PG class), and they went into service between 1993 and 1995.

The fame of the missile patrol boat began with the sinking of the Israeli destroyer *Eilat,* the first warship to be sunk by missiles alone. This was further heightened when some French built Israeli patrol boats left Cherbourg in defiance of a French embargo.

A confusion of letters

Although the patrol boat is, as its name obviously explains, a boat that patrols, the concept is an old one and was applied to all small capacity vessels that carried out minor tasks. Owing to the limited armaments that they could carry and the strength of possible rivals they could deal with, these vessels were rarely taken out of domestic waters, where they performed duties related to what is now known as coastal impermeability. Consequently, the naval lexicon describes them as coastguard vessels, warning ships, cutters, pinnaces, vedettes and other similar concepts. The appearance of internal combustion engines brought about a series of small vessels that were classified more in accordance to their particular missions, such as SC, PC, ML, PT, MTB and many more names. Sometimes,

TRANSPORTABLE ON A C-5 GALAXY

The Pegasus was inspired by off-shore sports boats, but they were designed so that they are small enough to be transported in the hold of a C-5 Galaxy, which means that they can be taken to any corner of the globe in a matter of hours.

the name made reference to the kind of weapons that they used, such as PT (Patrol Torpedo). On others it would include the form of propulsion they used, MTB (Motor Torpedo Boat) or MGB (Motor GunBoat) for instance. On other occasions it would refer just to the propulsion system as is the case of the ML (Motor Launch) or sometimes other concepts such as SGB (Steam Gun Boat) or RML (Rescue Motor Launch).

Other countries also had confusing

ELECTRONICS

The Barzan have Thomson CSF MRR air-surface radar and Kelvin Hughes 1007 navigation radar, both on the top. In addition, they have Signaal STING for fire control, Signaal STING for optronic direction and a Signaal IRSCAN electro-optic scanner.

terminology for their vessels as well as are the cases of the German R (Raumboote) and S (Scnellnoote), the Italian MAS (Motoscafi Asalto Siluranti), the Swedish TB (Torpedo Bät) and the Spanish LAS (Lancha Anti Submarina) and LT (Lancha Torpedera).

NATO tried to standardize the classification system, and refers to all small capacity vessels as P (Patrol) and all those for mine warfare as M. Auxiliary vessels, regardless of their size, have an A suffix.

The missile launch

For years, the most ominous threat to any ship was the torpedo, which is able to sink or seriously damage any vessel.

Towards the end of the 1950s, the Soviet Union decided to replace torpedos with missiles. However, missiles were not popular at the time, and NATO viewed the idea scornfully. The idea was to reduce the differences between the USSR's fleet and that of its perceived enemy, the USA and NATO. The sinking of the Israeli destroyer *Eilat* by Soviet SS-N-2 Styx missiles, in October 1967 by a Russian built Egyptian Komar class patrol boat came as a surprise to Western countries, and brought two important matters into the limelight. Firstly, the possibility that the USSR could become a fearsome naval enemy and, secondly, the appearance of a new weapon that not only seemed perfectly viable, but was also extremely dangerous.

From that day on, all governments and in

WASPADA CLASS

The Sultanate of Brunei has, among others, three Waspada class boats, armed with SSM Exocet MM38, two 30 m GCM-801 guns (I x II) and two 7.62 mm machine guns. From the year 2001 the new Yarrow type will come into service, somewhat larger and better armed.

KILIÇ CLASS

Turkey has one of the most powerful fleets in the Mediterranean, and recently expanded it with the inclusion of the *Kiliç*. The first of a series built by Lürssen in Germany in 1998, and that will soon be followed by two twin vessels that shall be built in Turkey before the year 2001.

particular those with sizeable fleets, began studying ways of dealing with this threat. Many of these countries actually owned SSM and missile launches that were being sold to countries that, in the not too distant future, could be using them to attack themselves.

These launches were given different names, although they all had the standard P prefix, which we shall use to refer to all missile and patrol boats to distinguish them from other vessels that are used for administrative purposes or OPV.

Modern day combat patrol boats

Nowadays, in the 160 or so fleets of the world, there are about 1,425 patrol boats of more than 100 tons, and about half of them are, or potentially are, missile carriers. Assuming that each of these can carry between 4 and 8 missiles, the total number of anti-ship missiles that the world can launch must fall somewhere between 3,000 and 6,000. That number is enough to cause considerable alarm to any country with a sizeable fleet. In addition to these SSM, there are also the anti-ship missiles that can be launched from the air, which could easily multiply the aforementioned total by 3, 4 or even more. The use of large warships is only within the capabilities of very few countries, those with enough economical strength to acquire, equip and maintain them. However, missile patrol boats

are available to most of the smaller and less powerful countries, being cheaper and far less sophisticated vessels. They can even fall quite easily into the hands of any sophisticated terrorist or Mafia group, because they are not excessively expensive or particularly difficult to operate.

Norms of encounters

Contrary to popular belief, these ships only very rarely attack at high speeds, reserving this for a hasty retreat, although even then, they do not always do so. Before radar existed, attacks were carried out at night and at low speeds, making as little noise as possible and taking cover in bays and coves. Therefore, being relatively small vessels that are not designed for heavy naval duties, they are more suited to coastal tasks rather than sailing for long periods of time on the open sea. For military reasons, they have quite small capacities, because a smaller ship is more likely to pass unnoticed, particularly so since the advent of radar.

Nowadays, apart from taking tactical advantage of geographical features as they have done

HAUK CLASS

The Norwegian Hauks are missile and torpedo patrol boats with different weapon configurations. The photograph shows the *Skarv* with four SSM Konsberg Penguin Mk 2 and two 533-mm torpedo tubes, one of 40/70 mm and the other of 20 mm.

SPECIAL SEATS

These small vessels (24.7 x 5.3 m) reach exceptionally high speeds and jump along the surface of the water, obliging all those who travel on board to use special seats, strapped in by safety harnesses and holding on to special handles.

in the past. These ships often try to hide themselves amongst the other maritime traffic in the area, and launch missiles from these positions, knowing that if they are discovered, there are only two options available: either to continue the attack, or to retreat. Neither of the two possibilities offers any guarantee of survival.

The philosophy of the project

A missile or artillery patrol boat is a small capacity vessel that does not exceed 500 tons or 60 meters in length. Anything larger would be considered a corvette. They have aerodynamically formed hulls that help them move at speeds of up to 35 knots, with SSM armament, and sometimes SAM, and medium and heavy guns up to 76/62 mm and several guns and machine guns of up to 20 mm. In recent times they have been used extensively in an anti-terrorism role and in the control of drug trafficking, and may therefore carry grenade launchers or similar. As for propulsion, they are usually equipped with diesel engines, although they have been known to use small gas turbines. Although they usually use propellers, hydrojets have recently been gaining

BOW RAMP

These patrol boats have a special ramp at the bow for launching and for recovering rubber dinghies at high speeds. Their maximum speed is 45 knots, which can be quite uncomfortable for the crew. They are propelled by two Ka-Me-We hydrojets.

BIZERTE CLASS

The three Tunisian Bizerte were built in France, in Villeneuve-la-Garenne, by SFCN. Although, theoretically, they should use cable controlled SSM Aerospatiale SS 12M, it does not seem like they actually do. Their armaments are two twin mounts of 37/63-mm guns, probably made in China, and two more single mounts.

popularity, and there are a few examples of ANT, such as aquaplanes, ACV and SES.

They have search radar and powerful EW equipment, as one of their basic functions is to avoid enemy radar. Some have sophisticated navigation systems, such as computerised mapping with satellite positioning. All have GPS navigation systems and navigation radar. They can alter their navigation lights to confuse the enemy, by disguising themselves as ordinary fishing trawlers or merchant ships going about their normal business.

The most important types

Of the many types of missile patrol boats that exist, some of the more interesting ones are the Waspada of Brunei, the Barzan of Qatar, the Indonesian Dagger, the Norwegian Hauk, the Turkish Kiliç, the Malaysian Perdana and the Finnish Rauma. We have only chosen one artillery variant for these pages, the Tunisian Bizerte.

TWIN MACHINE GUNS

On each side of the bridge, there is a twin 12.7-mm machine gun, with automatic feed. Though they can be exchanged for a 40-mm grenade launcher, or one of many automatic weapons available.

ELECTRONIC WARFARE

The AN/APR-39 radar alarm equipment is located at the top of the mast. It is a highly efficient reliable aerial ESM, and its small size and light weight make it ideal for such a small boat.

RADAR

Their are two radar, a Sperry RASCAR for surface reconnaissance, on E/F/I/J bands, and another Raytheon SPS-64 (V09) for navigation on band I. Above the bridge there is a SATCOM communication system.

NOCTURNAL VISOR

On the roof of the bridge is a special foldable visor that serves as a gyroscopic repeater, night visor and as a telescope.

BOW GUN

On the forecastle, there is a Bushmaster Mk 96 25/87-mm gun, with excellent firepower and a laser/infrared sight.

CHANGING LIGHTS

There are a number of lights on the mast, that turn on and off in order to confuse observers, and give the wrong impression of the boat's genuine purpose.

GUN AND GRENADE LAUNCHER

At the stern, on the superstructure deck, they have a special twin mount for a 40-mm grenade launcher and a 20-mm gun.

SAM STINGER MISSILES

Above the waist deck are two containers for six Stinger missiles that are fired individually from the shoulder of the server. There can be several and they can use different missiles.

PAXMAN ENGINES

Propulsion is obtained via four Paxman Valenta 16RP 200 CM engines of 3,350 HP, with a low high power to weight ratio. They are connected to four propellers. These take the boat up to maximum speeds of 35 knots, with a range of 2,500 miles at 12 knots. They can also travel quickly at low speeds if surprise is required.

STERN PLATFORM

These ships displace 334 tons and are 52 meters long, 7.9 m wide and have a draught of 2.4 m. At the stern they have a small balcony/platform, from where SEAL and other divers enter the water.

Traditionally, combat ships have been re-supplied by different auxiliary vessels, or whenever possible at a port, where the crew could also rest. Nowadays, things are very different, and ships can be replenished at sea. This obviously saves a lot of time, but is also an extremely complex and sometimes very dangerous operation.

Fuel supply at sea

In the First World War, and in particular when the battle for the seas and anti-submarine warfare came into play, ships had to stay at sea for long periods of time. They had to be refuelled by transport ships, although this could only be done safely when the sea was calm. The process was particularly arduous when coal-fire ships had to be refuelled.

Refuelling became much easier and more convenient with the adoption of fuels oil. Gone were the days of transferring sack loads of coal back and forth, and tipping the coal into bunkers and subsequently plastering the ships in a

DIFFERENT SUPPORTS

Although all are, in practice, designed for multipurpose use, different kinds of supports are used for different tasks. The photograph shows the British *Fort Victoria*, with arch shaped supports, these ships are not fitted with derricks as in the past. These can be compared to those in the above photo, which show the outstretched derrick.

blanket of black coal dust. Now, all that was needed was a pump and a hose.

However, other supplies, such as ammunition and provisions, still had to be loaded at protected bases, although at times ships were re-provisioned at sea if the weather was clam enough. Alternatively a safe port could be used as well, were as long as necessary was taken to load the ammunition and provisions.

Constant operation

However, in the Second World War, things changed radically. There simply were not enough re-supply units to cope with such long and large-scale military campaigns.

Therefore, new methods of supply had to be designed, or otherwise ships were going to spend most of their time travelling back and forth between their operational. Therefore, chains of supply were set up to transport the necessary material from ports to the forward bases. Similar methods were even used for the maintenance and repair of the ships that had battle damage and general wear and tear. The ingenious methods that some navies came up with are now looked back on as legendary, as they had to concoct ways of replenishing ships that had not been built to be able to do so. They even went as far as converting ships that were designed only as warships into supply ships. Examples include the German XIV type submarines (nicknamed the "Milich Cows"), which could carry up to 423 tons of fuel and four torpedos; the Italian transport's *Romolo* and *Remo,* the only two of the twelve planned to be built, which could carry 610 tons; or those that supplied Japanese seaplane bases. Not forgetting, either, the US

POLES
The two fuel replenishment ships that are used by the German navy have lower supports than would normally be used, accompanied by an articulated pole from which the hose can be suspended.

Navy's own submarines that were used for intelligence, evacuation and replenishment missions in those dark years.

Total logistic support

From the 1970s, as a result of the need to replenish groups of submarines based around their CVS (originally more or less modified Essex aircraft carriers), AOR ships became an absolute necessity, that is to say, ships that could simultaneously supply both ammunition and fuel. They were given less weapons than an

FLIGHT DECK
Another differentiating feature of more modern supply ships is a wider and less obstructed flight deck. Heavy helicopters can carry out VERTREP operations here. Hangars are optional, although normally preferable, because they can be used to maintain the aircraft.

by employing a three-stage replenishment system. This involves ships collecting supplies from bases and land supply centers and then transporting them across the sea to AOE's. AOE's then take them to the areas in which the ships are operating, and transfer the supplies. Warships can then pick up what is needed, and that way stay operational. The main objective of this system is to ensure the delivery in as short a time as possible, of anything that might be needed to keep ships and airplanes operational (fuels, lubricants, spare parts, accessories, electronics, etc). Together with missiles, ammunition and bombs for the operations to be carried out. And most importantly food and other provisions for the crews.

AOE, and are slower as well, by about one third. This was based on cost/effectiveness studies, although they were at times expected to serve as substitutes for AOE.

Until certain operations had been carried out in the early 1970s, it was almost impossible to tell the real difference between the two types of ship. Towards the end of the decade it was clear that combat groups with aircraft carriers needed AOE's, because an AOR could not guarantee to be fully operational due to their low capacity for provisions and ammunition. To the extent that it would need to return to its base to re-supply far more frequently than a AOE.

A deluge of supplies

The Gulf War provided enough proof that the maintenance of a combat fleet involved the need for an enormous amount of supplies. Possibly the least important of these was the most crucial from the crew's point of view, i.e. provisions. Nevertheless, modern day warfare can use up considerable quantities of armaments in a matter of only a few hours, and these have to be replaced quickly if units are to remain operative. In addition, sailing at high speeds means rapid fuel consumption, particularly in the case of aircraft carriers, whose flight operations constantly test fuel and armament supplies to the limit.

The only way to deal with such demands is

CLOSE TOGETHER
There is only a narrow gap between the two ships carrying out replenishment operations, which makes the operation quite dangerous. The ship on the right is 19.5 meters wide, and the ship on the left reaches 29 meters at the flight deck. Bearing these measurements in mind, you can appreciate how close together the vessels are.

STREAM REPLENISHMENT
The first to use STREAM systems were the Americans. The supply ships and the receivers are positioned alongside each other and travel at speeds of around 12 to 15 knots and little more than 100 feet (30 meters) apart.

Supply systems

Nowadays, practically every navy has adapted the methods that the US Navy first devised, and use the same names and equipment.

The constant exercises between different ships are known as PASEX (PASsing EXercises). With the advent of permanently active squadrons that comprise vessels from different countries, such as Stanaforlant, Stanaformed, Stanaforchan and so on. Together with the periodic exercises between different NATO countries, has led to all modern ships having UNREP (UNderway REPlenishment) features.

The basic conditions of any UNREP ship must include capabilities for CONREP (CONnected REPlenishment) for parallel replenishment, and VERTREP (VERTical REPlenishment).

CONREP systems

The common factor of all these systems is the method two vessels are connected together so that supplies may be transferred between the two.

The most common CONREP methods are parallel or underway transfer, or STREAM (Standard Tensioned Replenishment Alongside Method) and those that supply via the stern (with or without towing).

STREAM

This system was first used in the United States. Generally, all 'alongside' methods use a cable called the jackstay that is kept taught by automatic winches that keep a constant tension on the jackstay. At first the hand rope used to haul the fuel hose or the stores between the two ships. But nowadays mechanical RAM tensioners are used with the hand rope being hauled across the gap winches. These make sure that the cable connection is taugh enough, and they are either powered by electricity or by hydraulic methods. The ships travel alongside each other and travel up to 15 knots whilst maintaining a distance of about

REPLENISHMENT (I)
Once the signal cable, the thin cable attached to the red and blue rectangular signal, has been cast and the hand rope has been steadied, the fuel hose is unwound, starting from the outside.

RAM TENSIONER
A RAM Tensioner is used to keep the cable taught from which the fuel hose is hung. They are hydraulically or electrically powered. At the bottom are three metal connectors though which liquids (water, naval and aerial fuel) are feed to the hoses.

100 feets between them. This is evidently an extremely difficult procedure that requieres expert handling of the vessels involved.

Although other systems have not been entirely neglected, it is normal for rigid supports united by a cable to be used, forming an overhead cable link to the reception point. The fuel hose is slid along this, and the hose then hangs from the stay by pulley wheels, and then moves across between the two ves-

REPLENISHMENT (II)

The double hose, sometimes triple if there is also a water hose, is fixed to a wide cone for improved control. The fact that there are so few people at that point is because they are letting go of the hose, not retrieving it. Next to them is one more man, holding square, red cards, who is giving signals to those who are pulling the end of the cable.

sels controlled by a system of winches and cables.

Replenishment via the stern

There are two ways of performing this kind of replenishment: either with the ship close behind the stern or with it positioned slightly to one side. This method has one or two advantages over STREAM, particularly the facts that it does not require quite as much skill to be carried out, and that it can be done in heavy sea conditions. However, the problem is that it can be a far more cumbersome method, because the replenishment hose must be lifted up to the loading deck.

Also, because the hose reaches the receiving ship by floating over the water means that it must have a completely watertight opening, complicating an already difficult process.

Of the fleets that used stern replenishment in the Second World War, the German, Japanese and Russian examples stand out, a time when such a system was called 'in single file'.

In modern times, many fleets have experimented with the viability of the system. The Spanish fleet, for example when it did not have

REPLENISHNMENT (III)

Once the tube has been received and connected to the points of the reception cone, the fuel can be pumped across. The photo shows how two men hold the signal cable that shows if the two ships are correctly separated. (left photograph).

MANUAL PULLING

Although the tube cable can be pulled by a mechanical winch, manpower strength is usually preferred, because the maneuver can be controlled more precisely that way (right photograph).

off systems, in which cargos in special containers are passed over ramps through doors in the side, or more commonly through the stern of the ship. This is still the most common method of loading and unloading in the maritime world.

Cargos are loaded on to the ship in containers via a special container crane, or on palettes along special ramps. Stores destined for a particular ship are clearly marked and located in a position were they can be easily located and identified, when the time comes to transfer them to that ship. All recent AOR (including the *Marqués de la Ensenada* and the *Patiño* use such systems.

a replenishment tanker for its own fleet (from the scrapping of the Teide to the introduction of the *Mar del Norte*), carried out trials with the CAMPSA tanker called *Calvo Sotelo*. The ship was provided with a Canadian Hepburn winch at the stern. This ship turned out to be well suited for such operations, thanks to the height of its freeboard.

Later, plans were made for both the *Marqués de la Ensenada* (previously *Mar del Norte*) and the *Patiño* to be equipped with similar winches, with the aim of giving the vessels the capability for stern replenishment.

NOREP (NO connected REPlenishment)

Of all the possible systems (even replenishment from rowing boats), the system used for centuries, would come under the heading of NOREP, the most common methods are VERTREP with helicopters and VERTREP with ships.

In the first case, the helicopter drops the heavy load that it carries underneath onto a point of the deck that is known, naturally, as the VERTREP point. This point is entirely different to the flight deck itself, and is usually marked in its own specific way. When dealing with lighter loads, a cable connected to a winch is used. It is not normal for the helicopter to actually land on the ship's deck.

Using the second method, stores are transferred from the replenishment ship manually via a jackstay

Ro-Ro systems

Although these systems are obviously not used at sea, it is worth remembering *Roll on/Roll*

VERTREP BY BOAT

Some navies use some of their vessels as elevators, and transfer supplies with them. The photograph shows one of H.M.S. *Fearless*'s landing craft waiting alongside the quay for the arrival of a truck with new supplies.

VERTREP ZONES

VERTREP zones should not be confused with the flight deck. The photograph shows a Spruance class destroyer and its VERTREP zones, the white squares on the forecastle and stern, and the flight deck with its own particular markings.

These patrol vessels are closely related to the concept of EEZ (Exclusive Economic Zones), a modern extension of the previous agreement over the control of national waters.

Expansion of sovereignty

Historically, the national territory of a maritime country included area of water adjacent to its coastline. In general, this referred to the area of water that was within three miles of the coast, with the furthest points assumed to be the main points of reference. However, there were fierce disputes that could and did lead to wars that were motivated by differences in opinion as to where the exact frontiers lay. In fact, over recent decades, such wars leading from the ambiguity of certain agreements (the most recent, perhaps, was the Falklands Conflict) have become the norm, with different countries discovering new ways of exploiting the resources of the sea, riches that range from fishing to oil. For these reasons, the area has been increased to 200 miles, the so-called EEZ or Exclusive Economic Zone. This refers to an area in which certain rights exist, although not everybody was in agreement, particularly those countries that

had considered certain areas as their own for years, and found their own economic interests in danger.

In the end, and not without a lot of tension, an agreement was made, but on certain occasions, especially when one or other country is powerful enough to support its own particular interpretation, such agreements have been modified by what can only be considered as force.

ALBORÁN OPV
As well as its four Serviola, Spain has two important patrol boasts that are comparable to an OPV. The photo shows the *Alborán*, with range of 20,000 miles at 13 knots, or she can stay at sea for up to 64 days.

Offshore Patrol Vessels

The coastguard vessels that protected the relatively narrow coastal strips could be small boats, because the area in which they operated did not require the use of anything bigger, but things have changed now that vessels must patrol a whole EEZ. What are known as Offshore Patrol Vessels (OPV) are often obliged to stay as long as two or three months at sea, just like the fishing vessels that they must control and often assist. As they often need to sail upon rough seas, they need to satisfy certain maritime standards in order to comply with their requirements without putting unnecessary strain on their crews.

Although fishing is not the only resource that an EEZ aims to protect, there being other resources from hydrocarbon to minerals to consider, there is no doubt that it is usually the one that causes most controversy. Therefore, OPV's are specially designed for use as auxiliary vessels for fishing trawlers.

In general, they are vessels of between 1,000 and 3,000 tons, although there are larger ones. They carry few armaments, because when armed ships are needed, the national navy can usually be called upon. They are fully equipped for dealing with fires, assistance and towing, and have their own hospital facilities and a certain amount of accommodation space for fishing inspectors or members of crews that have been rescued.

They are usually spacious and comfortable to live in, because they are designed in the

US COAST GUARD

The United States Coast Guard owns even more ships than Canada, and though the ships are smaller, they are of greater military importance. The photograph shows the powerfully armed cutter, *Dallas*, of the Hamilton class (12 ships). The USCG has a total of nearly 2000 vessels of all sizes and types, more than 120 helicopters and some 70 airplane.

P-400 CLASS

The French Marine Nationale has ten P-400 class patrol vessels. They are specially designed as colonial vessels and operate in the Antilles, Guyana, Numea, Mayotte, Tahiti, Reunion and one in Cherbourg for rest and repair. The photo shows *La Glorieuse*.

knowledge that crews have to spend a long time on board together. This is a situation that can produce a lot of personal tension between the crew, and that the possibilities of this occurring are considerably reduced if they are given the chance of a little privacy.

Although there are no exact norms in this particular respect, the archetypal OPV is a sizeable and seaworthy vessel, powered by diesel engines, with large fuel reserves that ensure it is able to say at sea for long periods. A large amount of special equipment can also be carried, and they often have the latest communication systems as well. Together with a flight deck and a hanger providing there is enough room.

Coast Guards

The coastguard service has existed for many years, although nowadays it is much more formal. There are all kinds of boats and ships that have been used for such services, including cutters.

Their main duty used to be the control of smuggling, whether merchandise or slaves. However, over the years several new tasks have been allotted to them. Now the normal tasks of Coast Guards include such matters as the defense of the coast and ships, the protection of the EEZ, pollution control, sea rescue and in extreme cases even to act as auxiliary vessels for its own military fleets.

As a rule, these vessels are classified alongside warships, but as a class unto themselves, with their own crews that are trained at special schools and colleges and whose personnel are not necessarily even related to the military world.

working more or less alongside them, and their work can often overlap. Canada in particular has a large coastguard fleet with no less than 103 ships, making its an important as the country's actual navy. The USA has even more ships, although they are somewhat smaller vessels.

The Flyvefisken

Denmark, a country with several important maritime responsibilities, planned the Standard Flex 300 in the latter half of the 1980s, an outstanding patrol boat for a variety of reasons.

It has highly modular armaments and features, being designed for vigilance, pollution control, combat, anti-submarine warfare, and for use with mines and as a minesweeper.

The basis of this ship is the fact that it can be converted for different uses by changing over modules of 3.5 x 3 x 2.5 meters, one on the forecastle and the other three on the after deck. To these can be added the removable tracks for up to 60 mines.

They are built in GRP sandwich form. They are driven by CODAG on three shafts; the central one being powered by gas turbine with a single fixed pitch propeller. The two outer shafts are powered by diesels with

Some countries have their very own colleges for such training, although it is also possible for this to take place at military, administrative, police or combined naval colleges.

In some countries the Coast Guard could be considered a fleet within a fleet, many have such large quantities of well armed ships that they are the envy of navies in other countries. Sometimes there are police and administrative fleets

HMS LINDISFARNE

The Royal Navy has eight OPV, two Castle class and six Island class, so named because each ship is named after an island. One of these is shown in this photo, the *Lindisfarne*, weighing 1,260 tons when fully loaded and armed with a 40/70-mm gun.

FLYVEFISKEN

These 14 vessels use a modular system that allows them to easily change their equipment because it is stored in containers of standardised size that are positioned in strategically located wells. The flagship is shown in the photo in its vigilance configuration.

variable pitched propellers. Two hydraulic propulsion units are also fitted, these are used when silent running is required and for mine-sweeping operations.

The Serviola

These ships were constructed by Bazán/Ferrol in the early 1990s and are a deve-

lopment of the Halcón of the Prefectura Naval Argentina and of the Mexican Cadete Uribe. Two other very similar ships were also built in liaison with Bazán in 1982 and 1983, at the factories in Bazán and San Fernando.

They have excellent maritime qualities, can stay operative on seas up to force 7, and can carry out aerial operations on seas up to force 4.

They are fitted with a set of enormous computer controlled stabilising fins to maintain their effectiveness at low speeds.

Recent disputes over fishing waters between Canada and Spain have shown just how capable these ships can be.

They are extremely comfortable to live in, with room for six additional people, as well as the crew and those who work in the hospital.

They have space, power and displacement in reserve that allows for a considerable increase in armament, with such items as a 76/62-mm gun and SSM missiles.

The Deirdre

The Irish Navy is made up entirely of OPV's, and the most homogenous of these is the Deirdre class. The ships are used for overseeing Ireland's important fishing grounds in the rough Atlantic waters.

The four ships have a computerised fishing control system, with an extensive database that permits the instant identification as to whether or not a given fishing vessel is authorised to carry out a certain type of fishing. It is able to locate as much information as may be needed for the task in hand, even information concerning previous activities involving the vessel.

The Fearless

Singapore possibly possesses the most unusual OPV's in the world. That is because its 12 components could be considered potential patrol warships, although they are officially classed as OPV they have a top speed of 20 knots. They are not unlike the Victory class used by Singapore, but are much smaller and cannot carry as many arms.

On certain occasions their armament includes Israeli SSM Gabriel missiles, or SAM Mistral, as well as a 76/62 gun and A/S torpedo launch tubes. All this converts them into potential missile patrol vessels.

VERTREP ZONE

On the castle deck, the Serviola has a vertical replenishment zone.

AUXILIARIES

The auxiliary electrical generators are in the same engine room as the main engines, there is also an additional compartment.

BRIDGE

The bridge is wide and spacious, with centralized controls for all the important equipment.

P74

OFFICERS' QUARTERS

The officers' quarters are spacious and comfortable on these ships, making long journeys much more pleasant.

CREW QUARTERS

There is also plenty of living space for the crew, including the all-important television and video, along with any other feature that you would expect to find in a living room.

ENGINE CONTROL

The main machine control panel can be used to control the engines, although there are centralized controls on the bridge.

BOAT CRANE

The RIB (Rigid Inflatable Boats) are launched and retrieved by a hydraulic crane with a telescopically folding arm, instead of a davit.

FLIGHT DECK

The flight deck is spacious and can cope with different types of helicopter, although in most cases it uses an AB-212.

DAMAGE CONTROL

The damage control point is centralised in a central office with direct communications to every part of the ship.

The media seems to have come to the conclusion that the concept of amphibious vessels is synonymous with the US Marines and Navy. To a certain extent that might be true, although this situation has been brought about by a number of circumstances.

Two worlds, two strategies

It is only possible to make an amphibious landing on a hostile beach with the support of adequate military strength and the securing of the waters around the area. It is very rare for such an operation to be successful if these requirements are not met, because the period of consolidation of the so-called beachhead is a highly precarious one for the attacking force. At this time, it is very much at the mercy of the opponent, and even though there have been a number of successful landings throughout history, they could just as well have been listed alongside an enormous number of failures as well.

Not long after the end of the Second World War, a war in which amphibian operations played a decisive role. The world was divided into two large groups that, to a certain extent, were very much related to their geographic and strategic positions, and each country's maritime and terrestrial strengths. This had a

THE LCC/AGF

These ships substituted the older Mount McKinley class AGCs, and others used for transporting staff, or other flagships or command ships, such as the *Belknap*.

ASDV LIGHTERS

These lighters resulted from the updating of three LCU that belonged to the 1600 series, and were equipped to support combat divers. Three units are known to exist. Two of them are normally based at San Diego, and the other at Little Creek.

considerable effect on the composition and balance of military forces on either side of the 'iron curtain'.

The United States, with the experience of two world wars behind it (wars which strengthened the USA to such an extent that it became the most powerful country in the world); realized that, as a maritime nation, it needed to own a powerful fleet to transport troops and equipment to anywhere in the world they might need to be.

The USSR, on the other hand, needed to construct a fleet that would be able to face up to the threat of US Navy aircraft carriers and nuclear submarines and that could maintain the country's international prestige, but generally

stuck to its traditional preference for military occupation by land. This is understandable, seeing as the USSR covered an area of Eurasia in which there are very few important areas of water.

The global policeman

After the Vietnam War, the United States was faced by a serious period of crisis, certain aspects of which have never really been overcome. Since that war, no American politician has wanted to be exposed to the national fury that accompanies any number of deaths or injuries, that come about as a result of that country's military interventions.

Whenever the United States has been involved in interventions and international crisis operations (Granada, Iraq, Somalia, the Balkans, etc), extreme care has been taken to protect the lives of each and every American who has taken part. The same attitude can also be seen in NATO countries as well, and also lead to controversy over the justification of such missions.

Therefore, the latest naval vessels, particularly those that are used on amphibious operations, make more efforts than ever before to limit the number of casualties. It is often the

case that the military effectiveness of a vessel is as important as protection of the crew.

Amphibious vessels of the US Navy

Although the US Navy's amphibious fleet has traditionally included a multitude of different types of vessel, they are currently limited to LHD/LHA/LPH amphibious assault vessels, LCC/ASGF staff and command vessels, LSD/LSD-CV/LPD amphibious or dock landing, LST landing ship tank and a group of LCPL/LCU/LCM landing launches as well as ACV/LCAC. However, the LHD/LHA/LPH have already been examined in the first book of these series.

The LPD 17, San Antonio

The first of these units is expected to be ready in 2002. It is said that they will be the most sophisticated amphibious vessels that have ever been built. The project has been constrained by one important requirement,

INTERIOR DOCK

The interior dock is accessed by the folding ramp at the back, and it is capable of housing many different types of amphibious vehicles, amongst which are included the VCA/LCAC, LCU and LSM-6/8.

DECK RAMPS

Shown here is a view of the different parking spaces on the exterior of the ship, reaching as far as the bridge via ramps. This practically doubles the amount of space for parking vehicles.

that the dimensions of the vessels are able to transit the Panama Canal.

The LPD-17 was designed as a replacement for 38 LPD/LSD/LST class units, and to operate alongside the LSD-41 and LHD/LHA. This would provide the necessary means for the adequate mobility of an MEF+MEB (Marine Expeditionary Force/Brigade). 27 vessels were originally planned. In 1993, the cost of each individual unit was budgeted at 800 million dollars, but this amount has since increased.

These ships are much bigger and can carry more vehicles than the LPD-4, although at the expense of the overall amount of cargo. Two LCAC can be fitted into the dock instead of just one. The hospital has room for 117 beds.

They will probably be armed with the VLS Mk 41 twin octuplicate modules, and a total of 64 ESSM missiles. Moreover, it will have twin RAM mounts, although when the first comes into service it may well use any new weapons that are available by then, even new HELW (High Energy Laser Weapons).

It will employ the very latest in sensor technology, including the new AEMSS Advanced Electronic Mast Sensor System). It may well also use the new Osprey V-22.

It should have a displacement of 25,300

THE AUSTIN CLASS
These ships are an extension of the Raleigh class. They are similar to LSD, but can transport higher numbers of troops and vehicles, and the interior dock is smaller. They have been continually updated throughout their military service.

MODERNIZATIONS
These ships have undergone such modernization processes as ACDS (Advanced Combat Direction System) Block 1, with QRCC (Quick Reaction Combat System) and SSDS (Ship Self Defense System), with the inclusion of weapons systems.

tons when fully loaded. The main engines will be diesel, and they will have a top speed of 22 knots, and having accomodation for 465 people (32 officers), plus an optional extra 25 and up to 720 marines.

The LCC/AGF

They serve as command vessels or flagships, and have far better living conditions for the crew and officers. They also have more space communication equipment. From these vessels the whole fleet can be controlled, the U.S.S. Blue Ridge is the ship that takes on this role in the Seventh Fleet in the Pacific, and the

U.S.S. La Salle is its equivalent in the Sixth Fleet which is based in the Mediterranean.

The LPD

The US Navy has, at the moment, a total of 11 LPD, or Austin class amphibian transport docks, which were completed between 1965 and 1971. They are similar to LSD, and can transport and accommodate 930 people, with nine LCM-6 launches or four LCM-8 or two LCAC or 20 LVT. From the year 2002 onwards, they will be replaced by the LPD-17.

The LSD/LSD-CV

These ships came into service in 1985 and are very similar to the earlier LSD, although they have better capacity and distribution. The series of 12 vessels is divided into two sub-series, the Whitbey Island and the Harpers Ferry. The former has greater capacity for vehicles, and the latter can carry greater amount of cargo though at the expense of reducing the size of the dock.

The Whitbey Island, LSD-41

These vessels were built between 1985 and 1992, they displace 15,165 tons when fully loaded and measure 176.8 meters in length, and 25.6 m wide with a draught of 6 meters.

They can transport 450 marines, along with four LCAC, or 21 LCM-6, or three LCU, or 64 LVTP, and two LCPL launches. An area of 141 m³ is available for the transport of loads on palettes and 1,161 m², including the four LCAC, for any kind of vehicle. They can transport 90 tons of JP-5.

RADICAL MODIFICATIONS

La Salle, an old LPD, started receiving office barges in its dock. This dock was later substituted by decks with several offices and meeting rooms.

The Harper Ferry, LSD-49 (VS)

Although they look exactly the same from the outside, they are very different on the inside. They have the capacity for larger loads: 1,913 m³ for loads on palettes and 1,876 m2 for vehicles. They also have a different interior distribution, designed to make it easier to move vehicles around. This helps the loading and unloading of vehicles enormously. These ships can also transport 90 tons of JP-5, and also carry the petrol and diesel for the vehicles.

The LST Newport class

Landing Ship Tanks were used extensively during the landings of the Second World War, in which they transported and deployed tanks and other vehicles. However, its flat bow prevented it from reaching high speeds and also made them difficult to steer. As a result of this, and particularly the landing at Inchon, in Korea, new ships were designed

THE LST NEWPORT

These ships have a lower hold that carries the heavier loads. On the deck, there is space to park 29 trucks, Hummer 4x4's or similar vehicles.

under the heading of the Newport class.

They have a curious look to them, one could even describe it as eccentric, with two large masts at the bow, which supports the apparatus that lifts and lowers the ramp. Part of the bow has to be opened for the vehicles to leave the ship. They are roll-on roll-off vessels, in every sense of the word, the equipment being loaded via the stern entrance or the bow ramp. The hold can transport 23 LVTP-7, 41 6x6 trucks of 2.5 tons, or the equivalent in heavy tanks.

The upper deck can carry an additional 29 trucks, or similar vehicle, but not tanks or LVTP, which are too heavy.

LCU/LCM/LCPL/ASDV

These are the lesser vessels that are used for transferring marines and vehicles onto the beach. There are several different types and series.

LCU can transport cargos of up to 170 tons, three heavy tanks or 350 men. LCM-8 carries one tank or 200 men. LCM-6 carries 80 men or 34 tons of cargo. LCPL tend to be used as the lead ships, controlling and commanding each landing assault.

The ASDV is an updated version of the LCU that serves to support groups of marines on special missions, and particularly combat divers.

> **BOW RAMP**
> The bow ramp is made of aluminium, but is strong enough to carry heavy tanks or any other type of vehicle. They are normally stowed on the forecastle, above the ramp that gives access to the hold. The two stantions support the cables and pulleys that lift it.

> **IMPROVEMENTS IN INTERIOR SPACE**
> The Harpers Ferry (in the photo, the *Carper Hall*) are modified versions of the LSD 41, although they are almost identical. The main differences are the sizes and positions of the interior ramps, and the bow rotation point (a small, round platform that turns vehicles around), which on these vessels is both larger and more operable.

Smaller models of the future

Conventional propeller propulsion could soon be replaced by hydrojets on newer and smaller vessels. Such vessels will, for the most part, be made of GRP.

At the moment, there do not seem to be any plans to build smaller LCAC models, although several studies have investigated the possibility. Though it may be true that the US Navy has been working on SES, nothing has been done with respect to amphibious vessels.

CHARACTERISTICS

LCAC displace 102 tons, and 169 when fully loaded (this can rise to a maximum of 184 tons), including the skirts. They are 26.8 meters long and 14.3 wide. The structure itself measures 24.7 m long, 13.3 m wide and 0.9-m draught. Four Avco Lycoming TF-40B jet engines, two propellers contained in nozzles and four turbofans propels them and provides the lift.

Without a doubt, one of the vehicles that has brought about the greatest changes in amphibious warfare is what is technically known as the ACV (Air Cushion Vehicle) or Ground Effect Machine, and more popularly as the Hovercraft.

Just like the films

Does anyone remember having seen a western film in which the saloon barman flings a glass of beer along the counter, sending it sliding down to the other end? Well, without knowing it, what he was doing was demonstrating the theory behind the hovercraft.

In fact, if we can find a way to create a cushion of air under any object that stops it rubbing against the surface, a simple push will send it a considerable distance. The barman in the saloon pushes the glass in a particular way along a wet counter and the dampness prevents the loss of friction through a thin layer of air. He simply has to place the concave shaped bottom of the glass over a small bubble of air. This way, the glass does not slide along the wood, but on a cushion of air that prevents direct contact with the wood and allows the glass to move along the

MADE TO MEASURE

ACV/LCAC were designed to fit into the docks of amphibious ships. The photo shows an LCAC positioned to a millimeter inside one such dock. The flexible skirts of these vehicles, which overhang considerably on either side, are extremely useful.

counter quickly. The small amount of liquid on the surface acts as an elastic connection and stops air from escaping.

In Cowes, England, in 1959, the British engineer, Christopher Cockerell, having completed several tests and overcome a lot of problems, perfected the SR-N-1 (Saunders Roe), the first ever hovercraft, or ACV, in history, although the Russians may argue that their technology beat Cockerell to it.

The extraordinary thing about the ACV was

that by floating on a cushion of air, it was the first amphibious vehicle in history, able to move from land to sea and back again without needing to undergo any kind of transformation process.

The potential of this new vehicle was soon to be widely appreciated, and it was not long before the English Channel was being crossed by a larger model, the SR-N-4, that took both passengers and vehicles from Dover to Calais and vice versa.

Nowadays, the hovercraft has become a regular feature of the seas, and there are even associations that organise sporting competitions for these machines, on grass, snow, land and water. Apparently, it is as easy to drive one of these vehicles as it is to ride a bike, in fact the people who drive hovercraft do not need any more qualifications than somebody like a normal bus or taxi driver.

The operation of an ACV

To begin with, an ACV needs a powerful enough engine that can supply the adequate mass of air to lift the machines from the ground. The air is prevented from escaping by a rubber skirt around the outside edge of the craft, this then forms a cushion of air for the craft to ride on. Having achieved this, one or more propellers are fitted to provide propulsion, together with an effective steering mechanism.

If it had not been for gas turbines, it is fairly certain that the ACV would have taken a much longer time in coming about, although nowadays there are powerful but lightweight models

ACV-36

This Spanish ACV was kept operational until 1991, when budget problems brought the project to an untimely end. It could carry a cargo of 14 tons, or a Scorpion light tank, or three Land Rovers, plus 70 fully equipped men. They were propelled by twin TF-25 Avco-Lycoming jet engines. They had a range of 145 miles at 45 knots, reaching maximum speeds of 60 knots. They could pass over two metre high obstacles.

THE LCAC

These vehicles can carry up to 68 tons of different cargoes. They are able to carry one M-1 Abrams heavy tank, four LAV (Light Armoured Vehicles), three amphibious AVTP or two 155 mm M-198 howitzers.

with gas turbine engines. When connected to adequate ducts, the right quantity of air is supplied.

The other important factor is the air retention system. If there is a sufficient volume of air and the vehicle has to travel along land or a flat surface, rigid sidewalls can be added to maintain the air cushion. On the other hand, if the surface is irregular and rough, a flexible skirt of rubberised fabric on the underside adapts the craft to the terrain and prevents the loss of air. How much can actually be kept depends as much on the quality of the skirts as the amount of air that the ducts can generate. It is important to notice that here we refer to the skirts and ducts in the plural, because owing to the complexity of the matter, a multiple skirt is needed, with many chambers and water jet channels, along with a powerful system of producing air. One of the flexible skirts should be made of neoprene, but even then it is inevitable that there will still be a certain amount of fricative contact, or drag, with the ground, and due to the subsequent deterioration of the surface, there must be regular and careful maintenance.

Pros and cons

There are obviously several strategic and tactical advantages of having a totally amphibious vehicle that is capable of travelling straight into the center of hostile zones at such extraordinary speeds.

An ACV is not just a superb auxiliary vehicle for transporting troops from ships to land during a landing operation, but can also be used

for the fast and easy crossing of rivers, swamps and marshland and for advancing across areas without any kind of marked route.

The height of the kind of obstacles a hovercraft can pass over depends on the height of its own skirts, and at the same time on the quality and type of materials that they are made out of.

Contrary to popular belief, the amount of thrust needed to keep an ACV in operation is surprisingly low. Therefore, these vessels are often considered as MCMV, because the amount of hydrostatic pressure on the ground is practically non-existent.

One of the biggest drawbacks of these vehicles is the large amount of R&D that goes into their development, and the need for highly specialised personnel. Not only that, but their TBO (Time Between Overhauls) is very short, which does not go along with military requirements. In addition, they are certainly not cheap to use or maintain.

Russian ACV

The now extinct USSR spent many years working out how it would make a theoretical

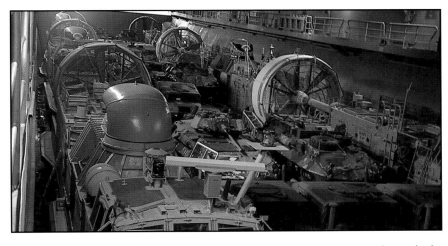

SELF SUFFICIENT
ACV can drive themselves to their parking spaces. This makes the operation much quicker and easier, and does away with the need for any kind of auxiliary apparatus, such as a crane. This photo depicts three US Navy ACV LCAC inside an LHD.

advance on Europe and occupy the whole continent before the NATO countries were able to reorganise themselves. If the operation were fast enough, there would be no time for any kind of reinforcements to arrive from America.

This would mean advancing at lightning speed from the borders known as the iron curtain to the natural limits marked by the seas. This would imply travelling 1,200 miles in only a few days. As ACV could travel so fast, anywhere between 40 and 70 knots, the idea

ADEQUATE FLOTATION
One of these vehicles is also able to stay afloat without any problems, even when heavily loaded. Therefore, unlike airplanes, it does not have to constantly rely upon its engines.

TOTALLY AMPHIBIOUS

The amphibious characteristics of an ACV are based on the use of the same propulsion and buoyancy system both on land and on water. They can pass from one surface to the other without any kind of change or modification.

of such an invasion suddenly became far more feasible. An invasion that would make the German Blitzkrieg (lightning attacks) of the Second World War look rather pathetic in comparison. For this reason, there have been class T4 ACV in Russia since the fifties. The nation has a lot of experience with these vehicles, and uses the largest models there are.

CONTROL PANEL

The controls of an ACV are more or less the same as those of an airplane, but much simpler to handle, because its dependence on propulsion is purely relative.

More than one hundred ACV have been kept in operation for decades, although recently the number has been going down, and one cannot be sure exactly how seaworthy some of them are these days.

American ACV

The USA has also used ACV since the 1950s, although the disadvantages of the vehicle have been met with certain scepticism. Until the mid 1970s, they used two JEFF-A and JEFF-B prototypes. The first LCAC (Landing Craft Air Cushion) were introduced in 1984, but did not appear to be fully operational until 1987. They now have 91 LCAC, all similar models, and the most recent to come into service was the *LCAC-91* in 1997.

In February 1994, the LCAC-66 underwent trials in Panama City, Florida, as an MCMV. Up to eight LCAC may well be modified for such a purpose.

Other ACV

Great Britain has been experimenting with different kinds of ACV ever since they first appeared, although most of these studies have been carried out in relation to civilian uses or by the Royal Marines. In 1983, the UK made trials and evaluations of the possibilities of

using a BH7 Mk2 for mine warfare. A BH7 Mk20 was even designed for that very purpose, and they would have used the same methods as US Navy helicopters, but nothing definitive ever came of the project.

In the 1970s, the Royal Navy based five ACV at Lee-on-Solent, and used them for a number of experiments. Amongst the models were an SRN-6 and a BHN-7.

GREAT MONSTERS

Russia has two enormous Zubr class ACV that are 550 tons when fully loaded, and can transport three heavy tanks or 10 APC, along with 230 fully equipped men. They could also transport up to 130 tons of roll-on roll-off cargo on palettes.

In Spain, the Chaconsa company in Murcia experimented with two ACV, the VCA-3 and the VCA-36, at its research centre in El Carmolí, on the shores of the Mar Menor.

Both ended up fully operational and were evaluated by the Spanish Navy. Not only did they carry out amphibious experiments with their TEAR (TErcio de ARmada or Armada division) but also equipped the VCA-36 for mine warfare and fitted it with a VDS.

The Gulf War of 1990 and 1991 created all kinds of problems for military budgets. Despite having spent so much money on these investigations, they had to be abandoned.

A new kind of amphibious unit has recently appeared, and apart from its military purposes, it is also an efficient auxiliary vessel when towns are affected by natural catastrophes.

Amphibious operations

The human being is an animal predominantly adapted to life on land, and for whom the sea is a vast and dangerous place. Therefore, any ship has to have some kind of amphibious element, because its basic function is always going to be the transportation of groups of people or of merchandise from one shore to another.

History is full of important amphibious operations; the first one that we have detailed information of was the Persian landing in the Bay of Marathon. About 10,000 men were transported in some 600 triremes, but the Persians did not know how to properly establish a beachhead and the operation ended in a Greek victory.

Important landings have been taking place for 25 centuries, though it was not until the failed Dardanelles campaign in the First World

SIR CLASS LSL

In 1964 and 1968 the Royal Navy received six LSL ships, named after the Knights of the Round Table. During the Falklands Conflict, the *Sir Tristam* was seriously damaged. Later, the *Sir Lancelot* was sold to Singapore and the others were radically modernised.

RAMPS AND DECKS

Most landing ships have roll-on facilities in their interior. Vehicles, even heavy tanks, pass from deck to deck along foldable ramps which, when they are not open, serve as conventional decks.

War, which ended in the loss of many lives, that the possibility of landing on a defended coast came to be seriously questioned, as it was again after the failed Alucemas operation. It was at this time that the amphibious ship was created in the true sense of the word.

It was the Second World War that served to show how extremely important a powerful, well-structured and capable amphibious fleet could be. The Pacific campaign and its 'flea jump' strategy put amphibious logistics and tactics to the test. The landings in Europe and North Africa proved the validity of the new ideas. In these operations, especially in Normandy, so-called strategic landings were put into practice. These landings had the primary objective of creating a new combat front rather than actually occupying a zone.

Further validation of amphibious landings took place in the Korean War. The landing in Inchon was probably the key moment when the allies were first able to establish their presence. The main consequence of that landing was the appearance of amphibious vessels; particularly those designed for landings, which had not only to be seaworthy but extremely fast as well.

The all purpose amphibious vessel

The ships used up until Inchon had very similar features, but they were by no means identi-

LANDING SHIP TANKS
The Newport class LST were widely used by the US Navy in the 1970s and 1980s, and other countries still use them today. They have a 1,765 m2 loading deck, and vehicles are unloaded directly onto the beach via a bow ramp.

WIDE DECK
The flight deck of these ships measures 100 x 20.5 meters, although on the *San Giorgio* and *San Marco* it is divided into two areas of 40 x 20 and 25 x 20 owing to the presence of boats and davits.

cal and there were several types. As a rule, the landings they were used on were extremely problematic operations, whereby the troops had to battle their way through the surf to the shore on their own feet, often facing enemy fire and burdened by heavy equipment. Therefore, landings were a slow and unpractical process in the nuclear age, throughout and after the cold war period.

When helicopters capable of carrying much heavier loads came into use, a system known as 'vertical assault' was put into practice. This system involves troops boarding helicopters from the ship and transporting them to the land, although vehicles and tanks still have to be taken ashore by means of conventional landing vessels. Some examples of operations in which such methods have been used include the 1956 Musketeer operation in the Suez Canal, the Vietnam War itself and much more recently, the Falklands Conflict in 1982.

The fact that, with the exception of the USA, there is no other country capable of operating a sufficiently large amphibious fleet, has meant that some kind of all purpose vessel has been an absolute necessity. A ship that could simultaneously serve as a base for

personnel, for transporting troops and equipment, with a base and deck for helicopters, and with a landing platform from which conventional boats or modern air cushion vehicles can be launched. These ships are usually designed for assisting civilians affected by natural disasters, although there are still many that do not have the wide range of capabilities that are needed for such tasks. These vessels are officially known as LPD, or Amphibious Transport Dock, according to the classification systems of the US Navy and NATO itself.

As well as these ships, the principal vessels

on such operations, there are also several auxiliary vessels that also deserve our consideration. These are used for transport and landing, and share many of the characteristics of an LPD. The fact is that the codes used in identifying naval amphibious vessels is an extensive one, and there is an extremely wide range of similar reference codes, but that have all kinds of different meanings. It is worth bearing in mind that the United States often uses different names to those used in other countries. This is perhaps due to the fact that the USA has many more vessels; they practically have a different type of ship for each different circumstance, while the ships used by other Western countries are far more limited.

The auxiliary landing craft used in countries other than the United States include the LSM, LSL and LST, which, along with the landing boats, play a decisive role in every kind of amphibious operation. Modern day amphibious vessels almost always have Ro-Ro (Roll on-Roll off) characteristics, which means that they load and unload their cargoes, in particular vehicles, by their own means.

INTERIOR DOCK

LPD and LSD have an interior dock, which contains the landing craft, this is covered by a deck. These ships have special ballast tanks at the stern that are filled with water this allows the stern to sink to a level which will allow the landing craft inside to sail out of the stern of the ship.. The photo shows the Intrepid, a British LPD, with all its ballast tanks flooded.

SAN GIORGIO LPD

Of the three San Giorgio, only the first two (*San Giorgio* and *San Marco*) have a raising entrance at the bow, with a watertight closing system. All three (the *San Giusto* too) have a starboard side entrance (under the red boarding point).

The Fearless

In 1965 the Royal Navy received the first of two LPD's, H.M.S. Fearless and in March 1967 H.M.S. Intrepid was commissioned. By 1982 these valuable ships were due to be decommissioned and scrapped as a result of short-sighted and ill conceived defense cuts; which would have hit the Royal Navy especially hard. However, in 1982 the Falklands War occurred, and the value of these ships was appreciated at long last, and common sense prevailed.

They are LPD ships, and can be considered 'classic' ships of their type. They have a large interior loading dock measuring 60 x 14 meters, with enough room for four LCU Mk-9 or their equivalents. They also have large interior decks that are connected by ramps for storing up to 45 four-ton trucks as well as capacity for a further 2,100 tons of equipment loaded onto palettes. As for their capabilities for transporting troops, they normally carry 330 men, but this can be increased to a maximum of 670 when necessary.

The Ouragan and Foudre

As for France, they have four LSD ships, the two Ouragan and the two Foudre.

The Ouragan have a dock that measures 120 x 13.2 meters, and a draught of 3 m, and a 900 m2 flight deck with two 35 ton cranes. An example of the kind of load it might carry would be 18 Super Frelon helicopters or 80 Alouette II; 120 AMX 13 or 84 DUKW tanks;

> **OURAGAN LSD/TCD**
>
> These ships, *Ouragan* and *Orage*, have a large interior dock for transporting a wide range of different cargos. The *Ouragan* in this picture is carrying an unusual load, a large EDIC (Engin Débarquement Infanterir et Chars) ferry, whose bridge, mast and funnel show out above the stern.

> **DECK LOADING**
>
> Apart from the space in the cargo hold, these ships also tend to use the bow part of the deck for parking all kinds of vehicle. If they do this, it does not mean they cannot also use the deck for aerial operations because there is also a helicopter spot.

340 jeeps or 12 fifty ton barges or a 400 ton vessel, along with 343 troop members.

The Foudre, meanwhile, have a 122 x 14 meter dock and a 1,450 meter flight deck, and can carry up to 1,600 men on emergency operations. They have enough water and provisions to stay at sea for 30 days with 700 men on board. They can operate simultaneously with four Super Puma or two Super Frelon helicopters.

The San Giorgio

The Italian Marina Militare ordered two LPD ships to a new design at the beginning of the 1980s, with a deck stretching from one end to the other. Together with a small stern dock of 20.5 x 7 meters for just one LCM, with enough space for the roll-on cargo that could be accessed from one or both ends of the ship, or by a door on the starboard side of the bow.

The *San Giorgio* and *San Marco* have a flight deck whose operational capability is limited by the presence of davits and lighters and also have a 76-mm gun at the bow. A third ship was added to the group in 1994, the *San Giusto*. She has been built to a slightly different design, which has given her a flight deck with fewer obstructions, in that the davits and landing craft no longer protrude from the side of the ship. She does though have the same docking facilities, though the bow entrance was deleted, thus giving her the capability to run up on the landing beach.

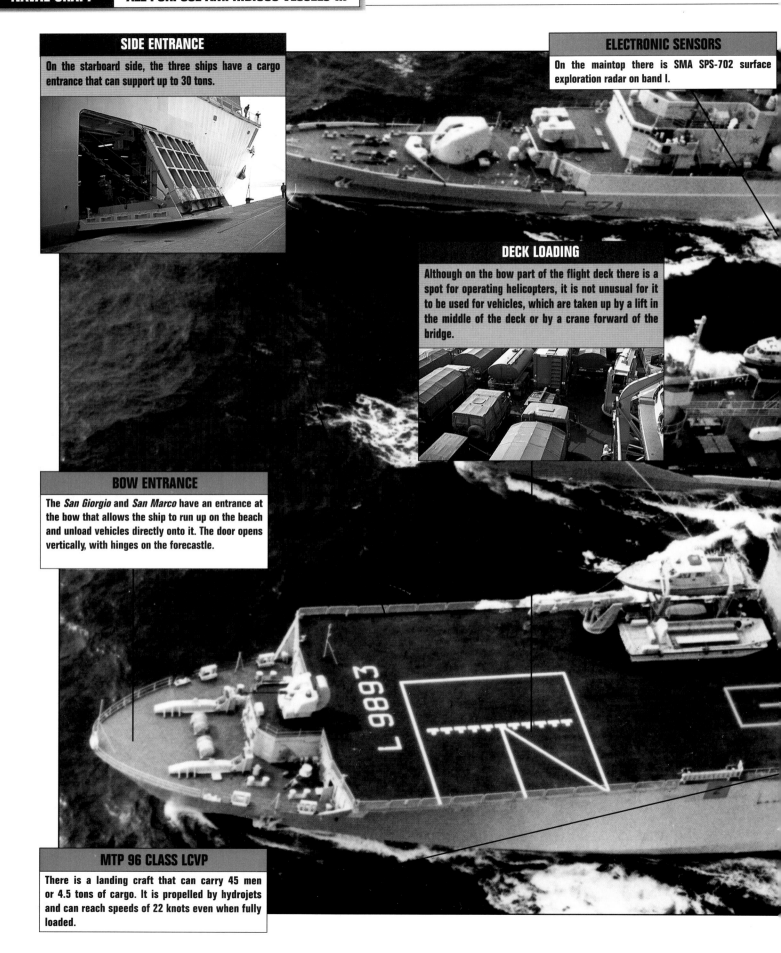

SIDE ENTRANCE

On the starboard side, the three ships have a cargo entrance that can support up to 30 tons.

ELECTRONIC SENSORS

On the maintop there is SMA SPS-702 surface exploration radar on band I.

DECK LOADING

Although on the bow part of the flight deck there is a spot for operating helicopters, it is not unusual for it to be used for vehicles, which are taken up by a lift in the middle of the deck or by a crane forward of the bridge.

BOW ENTRANCE

The *San Giorgio* and *San Marco* have an entrance at the bow that allows the ship to run up on the beach and unload vehicles directly onto it. The door opens vertically, with hinges on the forecastle.

MTP 96 CLASS LCVP

There is a landing craft that can carry 45 men or 4.5 tons of cargo. It is propelled by hydrojets and can reach speeds of 22 knots even when fully loaded.

LIFT

To take loads up from the hold to the deck, there is a 10-ton lift whose hatchway is always conveniently marked.

AREA FOR BOATS

The three MTM 217 class LCM that each ship has are usually kept at the bow, one in the dock and the other two over the hold. The dock is reached via a 70-ton crane bridge. Each LCM carries 30 tons, displaces 64, has a crew of three men, and can reach speeds of up to 9 knots.

FLOODED DOCK

The dock can be flooded, in the photo with an LCM in it, and it can be covered by a metal roof that is as resistant as the rest of the hold. It is vertically folded by hydraulic pistons.

FAST ACCESS TO THE BRIDGE

The bridge can be rapidly accessed from the exterior, which means there is no problem getting from the flight deck to the bridge.

O f all the amphibious vessels that have been used effectively for humanitarian missions, there is only one that can claim to have carried out a completely successful mission.

Shared financing

These days almost every country's defense budget is being subjected to constant cutbacks (in some countries more than others), which has led to the ingenious idea of shared financing, in general limited to amphibious vessels and patrol boats. The former are units that are appropriate for assisting civilians on certain occasions, which makes them of interest for departments dealing with interior, governmental and social matters. Patrol boats, on the other hand, are of interest to the food and fishing industries, and even to tourism, as well as those departments involved in such affairs as immigration.

Other more specific cases include the Thai aircraft carrier *Chakri Naruebet*, financed by several ministries, or hydrographic vessels that are chartered out for special missions. Diving bases in which a diver carries out underwater historical investigations, or mine warfare, which are all crucial for the maintenance of open lines of maritime communication.

In the specific case of the Spanish amphibious vessel, *Galicia L5*, these humanitarian duties have been served during the so-called Alpha-Charlie operation that transported

STARBOARD VIEW
On this side, there is the large bow door and one of the accesses, nearer the stern and under the crane. On the same level as the decks are the corridors that lead off the ship.

INTENSIVE CARE UNIT
The hospital zone of the vessel has its own fully equipped and computerized ICU with six beds.

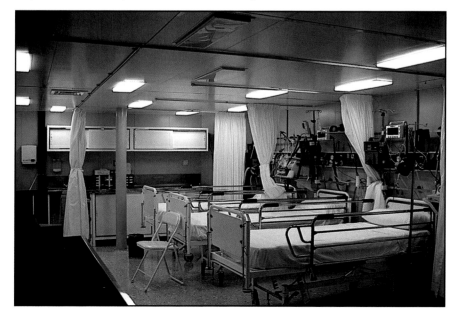

people and aid to the Central American countries that were devastated by the hurricane Mitch. This operation could be considered as the first one in history to be carried out by a warship in a foreign country, certainly on such a large scale and organised governmentally.

Operation Alpha-Charlie

This humanitarian mission performed by the *Galicia* (the *Pizarro* L-42 performed a similar one at a later date) lasted from the 22nd of November 1998 to the 17th of January 1999. Fourteen containers and 1,113 palettes containing all kinds of material for humanitarian aid were transported. Twenty-seven towns were assisted, with 32 tons of material delivered by helicopter and 15 tons by Hummer jeeps.

There were 4,848 medical interventions, of which 2,828 took place in isolated areas that could only be reached by helicopter, 1,390 in hospitals and local health centers and 630 on the actual ship, including 27 surgical operations, many of which were matters of life and death. There were also 13 evacuations.

The three AB-212 helicopters were used 104 times, totalling 115.2 hours of flight.

Most of the activity took place in Nicaragua and Honduras, the two countries worst affected by hurricane Mitch. The mission took a total of 57 days, covering a total of 11,550 miles and passing through the Panama Canal on two occasions (12th of December and 1st January).

Spanish-Dutch amphibious vessels

Following on from their participation in the NFR 90 program, EN Bazán developed several projects in conjunction with NEVESBU, a Dutch project and ship construction office, the fruits of which were the Patiño/Amsterdam logistic vessels and the Galicia/Rotterdam amphibious vessels.

The project began in 1990, the definition phase started in 1992 and lasted until December 1993. The MOU (Memorandum of Understanding) was signed in September 1993, and was followed by a series of steel elaboration tasks.

The Galicia

This excellent ship was built in accordance to the modular integrated construction method, an extraordinarily fast and safe system.

She was launched when she was 70 per cent complete, and the completion process on the floating vessel took less than a year, beginning on the 21st of July 1997 and ending on the 29th of April 1998. The first block was mounted on the 31st of May 1996. The total construction time, without counting the steel elaboration phase, therefore took 23 months. Eighty-seven per cent of the materials were of Spanish origin. Around 2 million man-hours went into constructing the ship. The ship cost about 147 million dollars.

Platform and habitability

The Galicia has been constructed according to civilian standards, though adjusted to different military features. Therefore, it has stealth capabilities, including slanted bulkheads, a communication system and military command, with NBCD (Nuclear, Biological and Chemical Defense) characteristics.

When fully loaded it displaces 12,765 tons, and measures 160 meters in total, 142

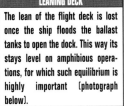

LEANING DECK

The lean of the flight deck is lost once the ship floods the ballast tanks to open the dock. This way its stays level on amphibious operations, for which such equilibrium is highly important (photograph below).

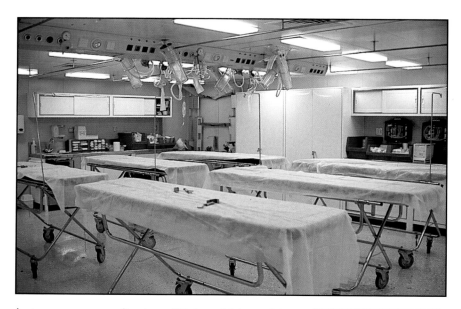

Space and services

It incorporates a 1,460 m² flight deck at the stern (56 x 25 m) and a 510 m² hangar (approximately 36 x 14 m) with the capacity for seven SH-3 Sea King or nine AB-212. It has a flooded dock of 975-m² (65 x 15) and more than 2 meters deep, and a breakwater and with a capacity for four LCM-8, an LCU or an LCAC.

She is equipped with two garages for heavy tanks or vehicles with any type of wheels. The surface of the main garage measures 725 m², and the secondary one is 285 m². It has the capacity for 130 APC (Armored Personnel Carriers) or 33 MBT (Main Battle Tanks) or the equivalent in other vehicles.

It has two storerooms for the Landing Forces (255 and 121 m²) with capacity for cargo on palettes and another five for munitions (total 289 m²).

It incorporates two cranes, one weighing 25 tons on starboard and the other 2.5 tons on the port side, an overhead crane in the hangar, and a gangway for roll-on vehicles. There is also an entrance on either side of the vessel, with an extendable gangway and crane.

It is equipped with two RIB's (Rigid Inflatable Boats). These are seven meters long and have 200 hp Volvo-Penta inboard diesel engines. It has replenishment points at both the bow and on the forecastle for liquids (DFM and JP5) and light solids.

between perpendiculars, 25 in width and its maximum draught at the bow is 2.86 meters. It is propelled by four Caterpillar/Bazán diesel engines, each one of 4.5 Mw, in two groups, the propellers measure 4 meters in diameter, there is also a 500 kW electric engine for emergency propulsion. They reach a maximum speed of 19 knots, she has a range of 6,000 miles at 12 knots. She is also fitted with a 1,500 kW bow thruster They can carry 887.3 tons of DFM (Diesel Fuel Marine) and 232.5 tons of JP-5 for helicopters. They are equipped with four 1,520 kW generators, and another 715 kW one for use in emergencies.

They can transport up to 115 people, with accommodation and services for a mixed crew of men and women, and can carry an extra 12 people in emergencies. There is accommodation for 543 Marine infantrymen and all their equipment, and capacity for 265.8 tons of drinking water, with an inverse osmosis system for on board production.

RECUPERATION AREA

Just before the hospital zone, thus forming a kind of entrance hall, is the area in which patients are examined.

INTERIOR DOCK

An enormous articulated door is opened at the stern, and amphibious vehicles go through it into landing dock, which can be filled with water when necessary.

Medical facilities

It has a hospital area of approximately 40 m² with six beds for diagnosing and treating sick and injured people. This is accessed directly from the hangar, a 35 m² pre-surgery room, two complete surgical units, a completely computerized 55 meter intensive care unit with six beds, a fully equipped dental surgery, X-ray, pharmacy, a refrigerated blood bank, laboratory, sterilization room and other facilities.

Weapons and sensors

For the moment, the *Galicia* only has two 20-mm guns. A CIWS *Meroka* mount has been planned, although an octuple VLS may eventually be fitted.

It also has Kelvin Hughes ARPA surface search and navigation radar on band I, IFF, SAT-COM, TACAN, and an SBROC ESM/ECM decoy launcher.

The Castilla

The same shipyard is constructing a second unit, the *Castilla* L-52, which should be at sea within the next two years. It is practically a carbon copy of the previous ship, but will have twin CIC, one for amphibious operations and the other for combat groups.

The Rotterdam

It took 27 months to construct this vessel, from the 25th of January 1996 (the first block) to the 18th of April 1998. It was launched on the 27th of February 1997.

It is the *Galicia's* sister ship, with a few differences, especially its diesel-electric propulsion system, which uses Stork-Wärtsils 12SW28 diesel generators and Holec electric motors. It has a bow thruster of less power. She also has different cargo capacities (170 APC and 611 marine infantrymen) and its loads can be very different (30 torpedos and 300 sonar buoys).

ROTTERDAM
The CIWS weapons can be clearly seen in this photograph, the mount over the hangar and another on the bow side of the bridge, along with the different sensors on both masts. At the top of the bow mast is the Signaal DA08 for air and surface search.

ROTTERDAM
Outwardly, the *Rotterdam* is very similar to the *Galicia*, especially if seen from certain angles, such as this view of the starboard bow. One of the most immediate differences is the difference between the two ships' funnels.

It uses a different configuration of armaments, made up of two CIWS Goalkeeper systems and four 20-mm (4 x 1) Oerlikon guns, with a more complete set of sensors, although one must remember that the *Galicia* has not yet received her full complement of sensors yet.

BOW BULB

At its bow, the *Galicia* has a bulb shaped addition to the shape of the hull, which lengthens the wave and lessens the amount of water friction, therefore increasing the ship's speed.

REPLENISHMENT POINTS

At the front of the bridge are two sea replenishment points, for both liquids and light solids.

HANGÁR

The large hangar can operate with up to seven large anti-submarine helicopters, such as the SH-3 Sea King.

BOW THRUSTER

The 1,500-hp bow thruster allows the ship to operate without the use of tugs. This means it can berth in remote ports under her own power.

LIGHT CRANE

At the stern/port end of the bridge is a light crane, weighing 2.5 tons for handling the the RIB.

INTERIOR DOCK

The large interior dock consists of three very clearly defined areas: the entrance, in which heavy landing craft can operate, the berth, and the loading and unloading area for LCM-8 lighters or smaller boats. In the background, we can see the breakwater ramps that stop water from getting into the parking area.

ARMAMENTS

For the moment, the only weapons on this ship are two 20-mm Oerlikon guns. The double arch on the right forms part of the communications set-up.

STERN DOOR

The stern door, once the dock has been filled, pivots downwards to clear the way inside for boats and landing craft.

FLIGHT DECK

Three AB-212, an intermediate helicopter for ASW, transporting casualties, establishing links and other missions can be used simultaneously on the wide flight deck.

ANT and military needs have introduced a certain range of synthetic materials to the construction of ships that, although they are by no means unknown in the world of sports, they are still relatively new in the field of warships.

Similarly, changing propulsion needs have brought all kinds of new, and not so new, propeller designs into the military and naval world.

Hi-Tech materials

Under the heading of High Technology, there is a wide range of new products and materials whose surprising and modern features make them extremely valuable, and often unavoidably irreplaceable, elements.

Composites

Without a shadow of doubt, one of the products that has most revolutionised light naval construction (or not so light, as in the case of a 700 ton fully loaded minesweeper) has been fiber glass.

The group of laminated or stratified resins (commonly and erroneously known as fiberglass) is an extensive one. Other polymers have been added to the group, such as aramids (Kevlar is actually just a trade name) and carbon fiber, which offer improved mechanical and chemical characteristics. However, these

PRFV HULLS

Laminating hulls in PRFV is one of the most complex tasks there are when it comes to using composites. In this illustration we can see the hull of the M-31 Segura minesweeper, still in its multiple mold. Air pressure is usually used to remove the mold, and each piece is removed one after the other.

SEGURA MINESWEEPER

These ships, totally constructed with PRFV, are one of the latest examples of HI-Tech being used in ship construction.

are already being challenged by the appearance of even newer products (it is worth remembering that certain resins can be used to make the crankcase of a car or a pistol that cannot be detected by X-ray).

A support and a resin

All pieces made of fiber glass are formed by a support that has been soaked in a certain kind of resin, which, once cured or polymerized, causes the piece in question to adopt the shape of the mold.

The support is, in itself, a rather soft and malleable element, meaning that the isolated resin is rubbed by a highly flammable product with debatable mechanical resistance. It has been used for military purposes for years, and there is evidence that it was used for making bonnets in the Second World War.

There are three large groups that make up what are known as laminates: resins (polyesters, vinyls or epoxies), textiles (fiberglass, carbon fiber or aramids) and several complementary products. It would be unwise to make a prediction here as to what the future holds in store, as new products are appearing all the time.

Resins polymerize, or harden, when a certain type of product is added to them, a process that can take anything from a few hours to more than a day, although it can take a few more days before they are completely cured, or dried.

GUN CASING

Modern gun casings of all calibres are also made using PRFV, because these days all guns are automatic. This photo shows the mold for a 76/62-mm OTO-Melara.

CME

On Spanish minesweepers, EN Bazán uses the most modern technology available, such as automatic saturation machines with computerised dosage and mixture controls. They use the Spanish made resin Resipol H-719, and the common multidirectional and unidirectional fabrics, mainly of 850 g/m2. They do not use any kind of *matt*. The hulls are laminated directly onto a steel mold which is in several parts, and the plates are laminated onto a multiple surface from which the pieces can later be cut.

All the completed pieces pass through quality control, where they are labelled and identified. Each piece is joined together by overlapping with a common margin of 50 mm. Each panel is 10 mm thick, made up of 20 layers of fabric, and the joints are spread out evenly to make one single, uninterrupted piece.

Other pieces

Nowadays, the casing or shell of a gun is very rarely made out of steel, being constructed instead with laminated PRFV on a mold. This way, they are far more resistant to external agents, although the mechanics cannot be compared with that of, for example, a 20 mm one made out of steel.

Other materials

A multitude of materials is used in the military world, many of which are used for highly specific and limited purposes. Among these are

VS PROPULSION

The German Company Voith Schneider only produces this kind of propeller; namely the four-blade K/KG and the five-blade G II, of which there are various models. This photo shows a standard G II.

IDEAL FOR BARGES

Azimuth propellers are ideal for auxiliary vessels, because they can be positioned where they will not affect the cargo capacity while at the time assisting with maneuvering. This photograph shows a Y-221 petrol barge belonging to the Spanish Navy.

anechoic tiles, which are attached to the panels of submarines, the fireproof materials that cover certain areas by their introduction into special kinds of paints and cables, RAM materials and even depleted uranium can be used to improve the penetrative power of sluggish CIWS guns.

VS PROPULSION

The blades of a VS propeller do not only turn on their axis, but can change their position in accordance to every turn of their supporting disc. This is why they are known as epicycloid.

New naval propellers

This group encompasses some highly effective naval propellers that are very different to those which have normally been used and offer a whole new range of attractive features. Even though some of these still use a blade as before, their unusual roles and positions mean that they too are considered part of this group.

Voith Schneider

This propeller is based on the theory of applying the principle of helicopters to water, and it allows a vessel to move in any direction over the surface.

The Voith Schneider VS was named after the Austrian who invented it. It appeared in the 1920s, when it was used on a tug on the Danube.

Its first appearance on board a warship was on the *Graff Zeppelin* in 1938, which had two retractable VS at the bow, in tandem and at midpoint along the hull, which would have served as auxiliaries when maneuvering the ship.

In principle the unit consists of a propeller that rotates on a shaft with the blades being

vertical, and their effect can be adjusted on each turn as they pass through a predetermined position. This generates areas of turbulence that provide the thrust for movement.

Its wide variety of aptitudes allows a vessel to turn within its own length for instance, and has a constant thrust at any angle or position. The system came into general use on German minesweepers during the war, and latterly in harbour tugs where maneuverability is important. It also has a low acoustic signature, which means that it is widely employed on many vessels. Later, when minesweepers appeared, they were used on these ships too; because they united the needs of propulsion in transit with those of dynamic positioning and that of a low acoustic signature.

Azimutual propellers

These more or less conventional propellers are mounted on the end of a vertical unit with the propeller being at right angles, and are capable of making complete 360° turns. The propeller may or may not be enclosed by a cylindrical shell and the number of blades varies according to the type of ship and the tasks it is required for. The amount of thrust also varies depending on the power of the engine that it is connected to.

There are several types, many of which are similar despite being protected by different patents. The most common are the so-called Schottel propellers (on which all others are

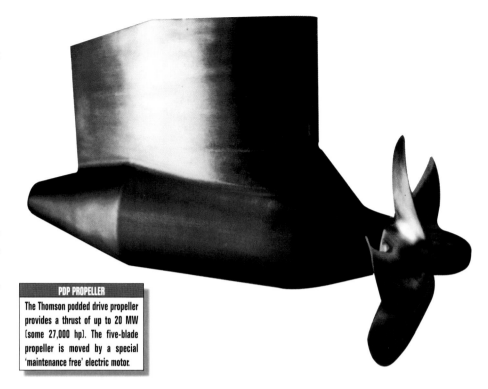

PDP PROPELLER
The Thomson podded drive propeller provides a thrust of up to 20 MW (some 27,000 hp). The five-blade propeller is moved by a special 'maintenance free' electric motor.

'Z' TAILS
This type of practical, robust and easily installed 'propulsion' is particularly apt for smaller boats. They can use diesel or petrol engines, and there are versions with only one blade (this photo shows the structure of one such mono-blade, without the blade). Others have two on the same shaft, like in torpedos, which counter-rotate.

based), and the French company Alsom's recent PDP (Podded Drive Propulsion), first revealed to the public at Euronaval'98. Such propulsion is particularly apt for auxiliary vessels, because they do not tend to obstruct either cargo capacity or maneuvering.

Z Tail

The Swedish Company Volvo created this type of propulsion. Originally used for maritime sports, It combines all the advantages of both the inboard and outboard engine, and for this reason, it is also known as the in/outboard.

The principle is that of a fixed inboard engine which is attached to the stern of a vessel, to whose exit some shafts and gears are attached, forming the 'Z' shape that gives them their name. There are some with a single propeller and others with twin counter-rotating propellers.

They are normally only used on auxiliary vessels, in particular RIB (Rigid Inflatable Boats) or semi-rigid dinghies.

Hydrojets

Although a more descriptive name would be something like 'water ejectors', or indeed water jets as they are often known, the name

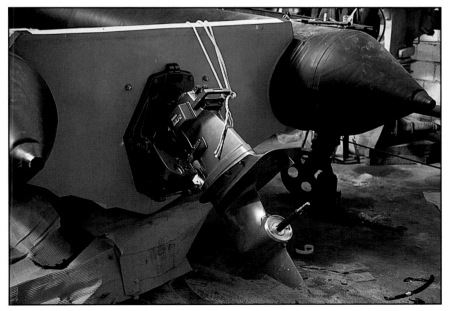

that has come to be accepted around the world is that of 'hydrojet'.

There are several manufacturers (Castoldi, Hamilton, KaMeWa, Kverner, Riva-Calzoni and others). They are generally used for propelling light and intermediate rapid units. They work with one propeller that turns within a tunnel that is not unlike an aerodynamic tunnel, with a number of specially shaped blades. The entrance to the tunnel is larger than the exit so that the jet stream becomes faster and more powerful, making it highly effective. The vessel can be stopped and steered by inverting or diverting the stream, which can be done by articulating the exit tube itself or by positioning a deflective panel. In fact, all the different patents are little more than minor variations of the same theory.

The propeller is turned by more or less conventional diesel engines, usually lightweight and high-powered because they are used on vessels that move fast, or by gas turbines.

Their most attractive advantages include their fast acceleration, the lack of propellers

HIGHLY POWERFUL

Nowadays, the hydrojet is even being used on some advanced merchant ships. This photo shows the stern of a MESTRAL class transport ship belonging to the Transmediterránea Company with twin KaMeWa hydrojet propellers. One is half-submerged in the water and the other is completely beneath the surface.

and shafts and rudders together with a mounting that is flush with the hull.

This form of propulsion is not only limited to naval purposes, and the latest advanced merchant ships have also been known to employ such technology.

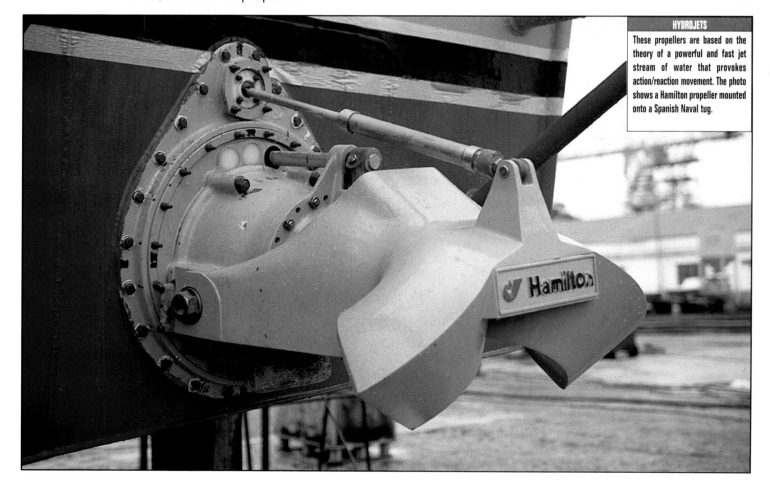

HYDROJETS

These propellers are based on the theory of a powerful and fast jet stream of water that provokes action/reaction movement. The photo shows a Hamilton propeller mounted onto a Spanish Naval tug.

It is much more complicated to maintain a fleet at sea than first meets the eye, because staying at sea for two months demands huge quantities of supplies, and even more if the fleet is carrying out a peace-keeping or combat operation.

The replenishment of a fleet

Different navies used many different methods of replenishment in the Second World War. Their main purpose was to keep the ships at sea for as long as possible, thus increasing their range and keeping them close to the operational area. This kept the time spent in transit to a minimum and reduced fuel consumption.

When circumstances permitted it, the US Navy also used what were called advance bases in the Pacific, to which all kinds of supplies were transferred and where it was even possible for the crews to rest.

All of this greatly increased the importance and quantity of auxiliary vessels. This is because to keep an operational fleet (or Task Force that can been made up of hundreds of vessels) in operation not only involves the continual supply of fuel and ammunition, but also many other products, whether they are for the actual ships, such as spare parts, lubri-

THE SACRAMENTO

These were the first AOE to be built, and are the largest up until now. The have a proportional quantity of armaments and sensors in relation to their importance, including the two twin Mk 91 SAM Sea Sparrow missile directors on top of the bridge.

FLOATING DOCKS

This photo shows the AFDM 10 *Resolute*, with an SSN Los Angeles on board. We can see how the keel and propeller of the submarine are covered by canvas.

cants, electronic equipment, etc, or for the crewmembers, because in order to keep up their morale it is important to provide them with products that range from mail to food and even entertainment. On top of all that, objects and spare parts are also needed for the airplanes and helicopters, including their own fuel and armaments, which are consumed in great quantities during military operations.

AO, AOR and AOE

Before the Second World War broke out in 1938, Germany built six oil tankers in

preparation for their use as auxiliary vessels for their raiders. Raiders were not considered capable of operating successfully without the support of a supply ship. The Kriegsmarine was only too aware that it could not achieve domination of the sea, obviously this would greatly complicate the operations of its raiders. The vessels in question were known as the Ermland class (Ermland, Dithmarschen, Nordmark, Franken, Uckermark and Kärnten) and they could provide virtually anything that a raider could need... they even had room to accommodate the crews of captured or sunken ships.

Two of those vessels fell into allied hands at the end of the war, and became USS *Conecuh,* AOR-110 (the former *Dithmarschen*) and HMS *Bulawayo* (the former *Nordmark*). The latter was scrapped in 1955; the former, however, was used in 1953 for trying out the new theory of 'one-stop-replenishment'. In 1956 it went into reserve, and was not scrapped until many years later.

The Sacramento

USS *Sacramento,* AOE-1, entered service in 1964, being the prototype of four identical ships. They were unusual because they used the turbines of two Iowa class battleships that had been cancelled (the Kentucky's were used on the *Sacramento* and the *Camden,* and the *Illinois* used those of the *Seattle* and *Detroit*). They have the capacity for 28,140 m³ of fuel, 2,150 tons of ammunition, 500 of dry cargo and 250 of refrigerated food. They have a

THE SUPPLY

These ships were built 30 years after the Sacramento, and therefore include a large number of modifications and additional features that make them more efficient. They have a Level III protection system for chemical, biological and radiological warfare.

THE WICHITA

The Wichita, practically the only AOR that was ever built, did not have a hangar at first, it was added later. They are crewed by nearly 470 people, which is still less than the ADE, which have 580 men (28 officers) on the Supply and 612 (27 officers) on the Sacramento.

maximum speed of 27.5 knots, and a range of 6,000 miles at 26 knots or 10,000 at 17. They have a hangar for three CH-46 Sea Knight helicopters or similar aircraft. They displace 53,600 tons when fully loaded and they are 241 meters long. Both ships are fitted with octuple mounts for SAM Sea Sparrow missiles and twin mounts for CIWS Vulcan Phalanx. They are equipped with decoy launchers and EW ESM/ECM sensors. The construction of a fifth unit was cancelled.

The Supply

These succeeded the Sacramento 30 years later in the saga of the AOE, coming into service between 1994 and 1998. They obviously boast several features that their predecessor lacked including protection systems for chemical, biological and radiological warfare. The AOE-9, *Conecuh,* was cancelled, and the money saved was used to alleviate the costs of the other three vessels. Eventually, however, the ship was given the go ahead, but under the different name of *Bridge,* AOE-10.

They displace 48,800 tons when fully loaded, and are 230.1 meters long. They can carry up to 24,802 m³ of fuel, 1,800 tons of ammunition, 250 of dry cargo and 400 of refrigerated food. They are propelled by four LM 2500 gas turbines and reach a maximum speed of 26 knots. They have three CH-46 Sea Knight helicopters. As for weapons, they have an octuple SAM Sea Sparrow mount, two CIWS Vulcan Phalanx, two 25/87-mm Mk 88 (2 x 1) Hughes

guns and four 12.7-mm (4 x 1) machine guns. They are all equipped with decoy launchers and EW ESM/ECM sensors.

The Wichita

These six AOR vessels were one of the few AOR vessels that were ever built entered service between 1969 and 1973. With their 41,350 tons of displacement when fully loaded and length of 200.9 meters, they can carry 27,822 m³ of fuel, 600 tons of ammunition, 200 of dry cargo and 100 of refrigerated

ARS SAFEGUARD

By law, the US Navy is responsible for the rescue of every type of vessel, be they civilian or naval, and they must have the right ships for the purpose. The Safeguard is prepared for the rescue of surface vessels and submarines, and is equipped with batimetric cameras and deep-sea divers.

food. They are propelled steam turbines, reach a maximum speed of 20 knots and have a range of 6,500 miles at 20 knots or 10,000 at 17 knots.

They are equipped with two Ch-46 Sea Knight helicopters; some of the ships do not have a hangar, though some of the class were fitted with one after they had entered service. They are crewed by up to 470 people. In recent years, they have started to be taken out of service.

The Cimarron

These fleet oilers were enlarged, or jumboised as the Americans say, so as to increase their cargo capacities (from 72,000 to 183,000 barrels, that is to say from 11,447 m³ to 29,094). They are the only oil tankers that are crewed by military personnel.

There are five ships (*Cimarron, Monongahela, Merrimack, Willamette* and *Platte,* which are numbered AO-177, 178, 179, 180 and 186), but they are unlikely to still be in service in the US navy in the 21st century. They will probably be transferred the navies of Brazil, India, Egypt or Chile.

Other auxiliary vessels

The US Navy has many other auxiliary ves-

OCEANOGRAPHIC

The Pathfinders are the most modern surveying ships in the US Navy. They are elegant looking vessels (with a similar shape to a yacht) and are only crewed by 25 civilians, to which up to 27 scientists can be added, depending on the mission and purpose. They use diesel-electric propulsion with twin azimuth Z propellers.

sels, but not all of them are on their lists. At the moment, the list has got much shorter, because so many of their vessels have been passed on to Military Sealift Command.

The largest ships are still the Safeguard ARS class (of which there are four), the three Emory S. Land AS, another Simon Lake and one AGSS, the *Dolphin*.

Of the other units, there is still quite a number with floating docks. The most unusual ship of all in the US Navy, has to be the frigate *Constitution*, a relic dating back to 1798 that is preserved in Boston. It was restored between 1927 and 1930 and then again between 1992 and 1996.

Military Sealift Command

This body originates from the Naval Ocean Transport Office, which on the 1st of October 1949 became the Military Sea Transportation Service and on the 1st of August 1970, Military Sealift Command. On the 1st of October 1987 the transport services of the Army, Navy and USAF merged to form USTRANSCOM (United States TRANSport COMmand). From 1992, and as a direct consequence of the Desert Storm and Desert Shield operations against Iraq, it was designated as the sole defensive transport body.

MSC's personnel are still under civilian jurisdiction, though in certain cases they come under military command. As for vessels, it is normal for a large proportion of them to be what are called 'sea civil', and nowadays, particularly with respect to vessels, they are contracted by companies in the service sector. Therefore, the state is not their direct owner, and passive classes come under civil jurisdiction and are not charged to military budgets.

MAIN AUXILIARY SHIPS OF THE US NAVY

Around 1978, the US Navy re-structured its auxiliary fleet and introduced new names for the ships according to their different functions. In 1996, the system was updated with new names and functions.

1ST GROUP OF FUNCTIONS	
Combat Logistic Type Ships (ships with a capacity for UNREP (Underway REPlenishment) for combat units).	
AE	Ammunition ship
AF	Store ship
AFS	Combat stores ship
AO	Fleet oiler
AOE	Fast combat support ship
AOR	Replenishment oiler

2ND GROUP OF FUNCTIONS	
Mobile Logistic Type Ships (ships with a capacity for UNREP for combat units, and also for direct material support to units operating at long distances from their bases).	
AD	Destroyer tender
AR	Repair ship
AS	Submarine tender

3RD GROUP OF FUNCTIONS			
Support Ships (ships than can operate on ocean waters and in different sea conditions and provide general support to other combat forces or land bases).			
ARS	Salvage ship	AGS	Surveying ship
ASR	Submarine rescue ship	AGSS	Auxiliary research submarine
ATF	Fleet tug	AH	Hospital ship
ATS	Salvage and rescue ship	AK	Cargo ship
ACS	Auxiliary crane ship	AKR	Vehicle cargo ship
AG	Miscellaneous auxiliary	AOG	Gasoline tanker
AGDS	Deep submergence support ship	AOT	Transport oiler
AGF	Miscellaneous command ship	AP	Transport
AGFF	Frigate research ship	ARC	Cable repair ship
AGM	Missile range instrumentation ship	AVB	Aviation logistic ship
AGOR	Oceanographic research ship	AVT	Auxiliary aircraft landing training ship
AGOS	Ocean surveillance ship		

A total of 205 vessels appear on the MSC's current lists, and they are identified by black, grey, blue and gold markings on their funnels. The vessels are often painted naval grey, or otherwise in some other uniform color, including some hues more typically used on merchant ships. There is a letter 'T' before their usual number and codename. Not one MSC vessel is armed, even if they are ammunition ships or oilers.

THE AFS

The combat stores ships (AFS) are prepared for supplying a vast amount of products, and to help with the task they are equipped with a computerized stock-keeping system. The Sirius class ships, the *Spica* is shown here, were built in Great Britain and were used for a while on charter

The ships of the MSC

All kinds of ships are found in this fleet, including the Kilauea class T-AE (eight ammunition ships), the Concord or Sirius class T-AFS (six combat stores ships, three of each class) and the Henry J. Kaiser oilers, thirteen huge 42,000 ton ships that are often seen refuelling combat units.

Other ships inscribed onto MSC lists are the Powhatan class high tugs and the Pathfinder surveying ships, even the T-AGOS ocean surveillance ships (known as spy ships). In other times, these ships kept close tabs on Soviet nuclear submarines, capturing all their noises and classifying and archiving their signatures in special databanks.

Different kinds of cargo ship also belong to the MSC, roll-ons or flo-flo, ships with floating docks that are specialized in loading and transporting other vessels, crane ships or ordinary general cargos, which are often seen painted black with white superstructures.

CRANE SHIPS

Crane ships, the *Keystone State*, T-ACS 1, is shown here, incorporate two or three pairs of 30 ton cranes, which can work in pairs or double pairs. They are used for unloading ships at ports that do not have their own unloading systems.

I n the short space of three months, in 1995, two practically identical and highly interesting logistic vessels, the Spanish *Patiño* and the Dutch *Amsterdam* came into service. Both have to be considered archetypal logistic vessels of an intermediate navy.

The *Patiño*

This ship was commissioned into the Spanish Navy on the 16th of June 1995, two years after construction started (on the 1st of July 1993), and a little less than a year after its launch (22nd of June 1994)

The construction of these vessels was a Dutch-Spanish project (Bazán-NEVESBU), and the first product to come out of this joint venture. Although they are outwardly very similar, they are not completely identical, particularly in the interior, where the *Patiño* is a specially designed ship for supplying aircraft carriers and their escorts. However, this does not mean that they cannot supply other kinds of vessels.

A sign of the importance of the *Patiño* in the Spanish Navy is the fact that the most important authorities in Spain were present at its launch. Moreover, the absence of this ship in the operations in the Persian Gulf (in which Spanish corvettes and frigates were among those that took part in ensuring that UN sanctions against Iraq were up held) obliged the use of Abu-Dhabi as a terrestrial base and of other nations' logistic vessels.

A long genesis

The first talk of a future Spanish logistic ship

BRIDGE

The very complete and spacious bridge is situated on the bow block of the superstructure, from where each and every one of the different services can be controlled.

was heard in 1973, when Admiral Pita da Veiga, at the time AJEMA (Chief of Staff of the Spanish Navy), made reference to a vessel inspired by the French *Durance*.

In 1986, Bazán carried out its first project with a logistic vessel, the B-130, whose scale model was revealed at Cosmo-86, and that bore a remote resemblance to *Durance*. During the summer of 1987, there were a number of changes made to the project and two different ideas were studied at the technical offices of Bazán-Ferrol and Bazán-Madrid. These production programs were based on what is known as 'Design to Requirement', and offered considerable differences, even on the outside, with one being a ship with just one island, and the other with two.

Meanwhile, the crisis in the Gulf was emerging, and the lack of a suitable logistic vessel was becoming increasingly apparent. The only one in

service since 1956, the Teide, was taken out of service in 1988 and not replaced. Therefore, on the 30th of December 1988 the construction of an auxiliary petrol tanker was ordered, called *Mar del Norte* (later called the *Marqués de la Ensenada*), which entered service on the 3rd of June 1991, when it was no longer so urgently needed. The project was based on a civilian petrol tanker adapted to the needs of the Navy, but budget limitations meant the ship was shorter than had been hoped. The ship proved to be more than acceptable, and for a while took part in all the operations the Spanish navy was involved with, including being part of NATO and UN fleets. As proof of its worth, in just 21 months it spent 320 days at sea.

At the same time, the aforementioned Bazán-NEVESBU collaboration was getting under way, eventually coming up with the project and construction of the *Patiño* and *Amsterdam*. The ships were finally commissioned on the 16th June and 1st of September 1995 respectively.

Characteristics and features

The *Patiño* displaces 17,045 tons when fully loaded, and 5,762 tons when 'light'. She is 166

CIWS GOALKEEPER

The *Amsterdam* has an anti-missile CIWS Goalkeeper mount. The *Patiño*, however, does not and has to use the Spanish Meroka, the only one of this personalized CIWS in the world.

PATIÑO

It is the most important unit that the Armada has received in recent years, not since the *Principe de Asturias* has a ship caused such a stir, offering extraordinary mobility to its operative groups.

meters long, 22 meters wide and has a draught of 8 meters. The main engines are two Bazán/Burmeister & Wein 16V40/45 diesel engines with single geared reduction, providing 14,000 hp sustained (9.68 MW) at 600 rpm, with a single, variable pitch Lips propeller, with 5 blades and a diameter of 5.70 meters. This gives her a speed of 20 knots with a range of 13,440 miles.

She is also fitted with an electrical plant with four groups of generators of 1,170 kW at 450 V and 60 Hz, driven by Bazán/MAN14V20/27

It can carry 6,815 tons of Diesel Fuel Marine; 1,798 of JP-5; 182 of freshwater; 100 of provisions (55 of dry cargo and 45 refrigerated); 240 of ammunition; 25 of sonar buoys and 9 of spare parts.

It has four points, two on each side, for supplying DFM, JP-5 and water; on the port side 680 m³ of DFM and JP-5 and 50 of water; on the starboard side 680 m³ of DFM, 115 of JP-5 and 50 of water. The larger capacity on the port side is due to the fact that the *Principe de Asturias* has its refuelling points on the starboard side, and therefore the starboard points, for frigates and other ships, have less capacity for JP-5. There is a fifth point at the stern.

It has four positions, two on each side, for heavy solids of up to 2,000 kg, and another two for light solids up to 250 kg. There is also a flight deck forward measuring 26 x 22 meters for VERTREP.

The solid cargo is distributed over the whole of the ship's interior, thanks to the wide corridor along the starboard side which stretches for the whole length of the ship, and along which containers and vehicles can be transported. Loading and unloading is all completely computerized under the control of the quartermaster.

The *Patiño* was built using MS steel, with a structure and services made according to Lloyds' specification, and stability criteria that obey US Navy requirements for winds of 100

diesel engines of 1,250 kW at 900 rpm. The main control panel is located away from the generators and the auxiliary panel is located in a separate compartment which supplies two networks of 60 Hz, one of 440 volts and another of 115 volts. There is also an integrated communication system, with an interior network of radiant cable that allows radio-telephone communication between any two points on the ship, and a highly effective cordless system that even works when there are serious breakdowns. It also has sloping exterior bulkheads that keep down the radar signature and an NBQ protection system with sprinklers spread over the whole ship. Due to financial problems, neither the bow thruster nor stabilising fins were fitted.

She is able to carry out aircraft operations in most weather conditions, she can also house and provide for the basic maintenance of three medium (AB-212 type) helicopters or two SH-3 Sea King. She has accommodations for a total of 180 people, Captain, 1st Lieutenant, 24 officers, 36 petty officers, 36 leading rates and 82 seamen, with a separate area for female staff. It satisfies NATO requirements with single and double cabins for officers, double and quadruple for petty officers, quadruple for leading rates and sextuple for seamen. All equipped with the corresponding lockers, cupboards and desks. It has a 20-m² library, a gymnasium, a medical center with ten beds, a surgery with radiology equipment and a dental surgery.

A POSSIBLE SECOND SHIP

The Dutch Royal Navy has announced a project for a second unit of the same type as a replacement for its current *Zuiderkruis*. It would enter service in 2003 and would be built according to an optimisation project based on the *Patiño* and *Amsterdam*.

AMSTERDAM

The *Amsterdam* substituted the *Poolster*, a logistic ship introduced in 1964, which make history in the Dutch Marines for being the second important vessel with facilities for a mixed crew of men and women in 1983. The first was the *Zuiderkruis*, in 1981, which had 25 women on board.

ted on the roof of the hangar and a few other minor details in relation to its electronic sensors and EW equipment.

It is hard to define the interior differences, but one obvious one is the absence of the radiant cable.

As for its features, these are not enormously different either. The loading and refuelling capabilities of the *Amsterdam* are; 6,815 tons of naval fuel (F-76 according to Dutch norms), contained in 15 main tanks; 1,798 tons of jetfuel (F-44/AVCAT), in two tanks; 182 tons of drinking water in one tank; 1,100 tons of provisions and 350 of ammunition. It has five refuelling points, four on the sides and one at the stern, with a capacity for some 1,600 t/h, 2,000 kg of heavy solids and 225 kg of light solids and it can re-supply two ships at the same time. It has a fifth re-supply point at the stern to replenish a third vessel, although it can only be used for F-76 naval fuel.

As can be seen, both ships are virtually identical. Where there was a large difference was in construction times, given that the *Amsterdam* took a total of 38 months (the first block on the 21st of May 1992; introduced on the 2nd September 1995), and the *Patiño* only took 24 months.

knots and stability being maintained with at least to adjacent compartments being flooded. She has the standard material for a merchant vessel, with warship communication systems, and a margin for further expansion of 150 tons and an extra 0.10 meters of vertical height above the centre of gravity. Its dismantling routes, availability of rooms and the movement of its crew all satisfy the conditions of a military vessel.

Sensors and armaments

The *Patiño* has combined air and surface reconnaissance radar with the capacity for air group control; navigation radar; flight control radar; TACAN and IFF. It has four SBROC decoy launchers for radar and infrared decoys, and two 20/90 mm Oerlikon guns.

The Amsterdam

Apart from its exterior design (the *Patiño* is uniformly painted in naval grey and the *Amsterdam* in a combination of light and medium grey), this ship is practically identical to its Spanish cousin on the outside, with the exception of a CIWS Goalkeeper gun moun-

HANGAR

The *Patiño* has a large hangar of about 225 meters, with capacity for two or three helicopters. The fact that it can hold SH-3D Sea King gives the ship a considerable amount of self-sufficient ASW protection, and this type of helicopter is also excellent for anti-submarine missions, just like the SH-70 Seahawk.

INTERIOR CORRIDOR

Along the whole length of the *Patiño*, on the starboard side, is a large enough corridor for moving containers and all kinds of materials on palettes or in barrels, including the mechanical equipment used to manipulate and tow them.

PROPELLER AND RUDDER

The considerable size of the ship and its propulsion and steering systems are shown by this photo, taken on the day of its launch, especially if you compare it to the size of the man standing under the central keel.

REFRIGERATED CHAMBERS

The *Patiño* has enough refrigerated chambers to store and conserve up to 45 tons of frozen food. They are built of stainless steel.

SUPPLY DECK

On the superstructure, between the fuel hose points, there are four cabins from where refuelling of up to three vessels at the same time can be controlled.

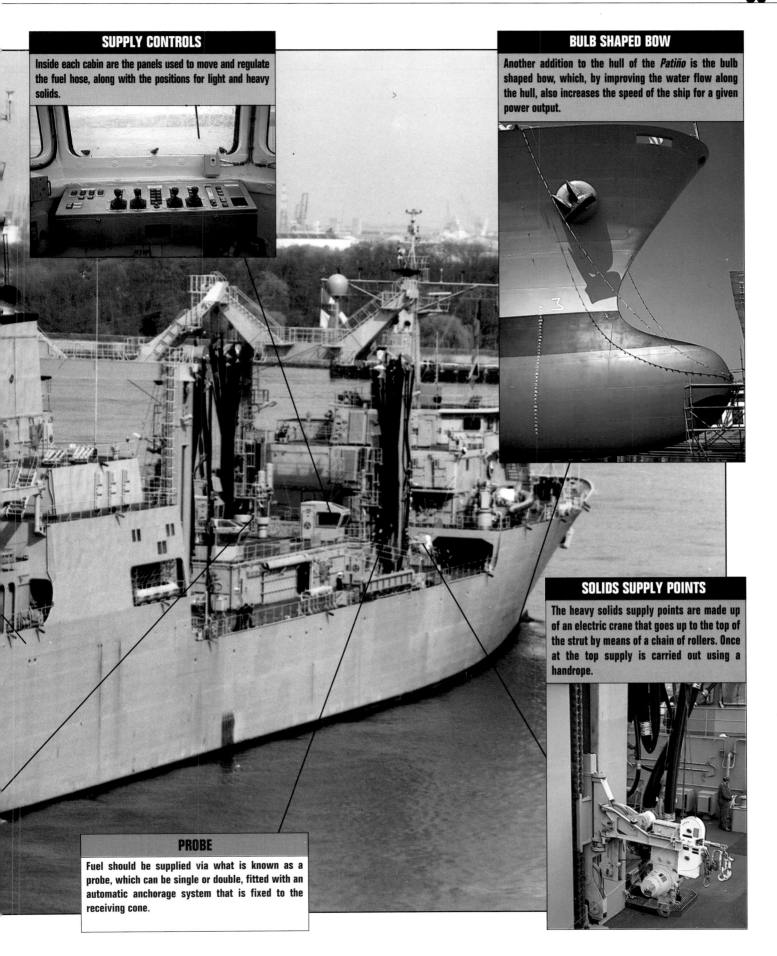

SUPPLY CONTROLS

Inside each cabin are the panels used to move and regulate the fuel hose, along with the positions for light and heavy solids.

BULB SHAPED BOW

Another addition to the hull of the *Patiño* is the bulb shaped bow, which, by improving the water flow along the hull, also increases the speed of the ship for a given power output.

SOLIDS SUPPLY POINTS

The heavy solids supply points are made up of an electric crane that goes up to the top of the strut by means of a chain of rollers. Once at the top supply is carried out using a handrope.

PROBE

Fuel should be supplied via what is known as a probe, which can be single or double, fitted with an automatic anchorage system that is fixed to the receiving cone.

There is hardly any naval fleet, no matter how small it may be, that does not include at least one or a few logistic ships. In the case of the smaller navies these vessels are bought or transferred from other navies.

The navies of the world

Among the 160 military navies in the whole world there are about 10,000 ships, not including the smaller vessels or those that are only referred to by simple letters and numbers. If these were to be included, it is quite possible that there are two or three thousand more vessels in existence.

Moreover, naval gossipmongers predict that over the next ten years a further thousand ships will be built, although a large percentage of these will be replacements for older vessels that have come to the end of their life span. However, many of the ships that are removed are not scrapped straight away, but are passed on to other countries whose economies do not allow for anything better. It is clear, then, that the number of military ships in the world is constantly increasing.

ARL *BUENAVENTURA*

This and its twin, *Cartagena de Indias*, used to belong to the Bundesmarine, and were sold in 1997 and 1998 respectively. Its original armament was retained by Germany, and it was left unclear as to whether the Colombians had any plans to rearm it.

ATS *SHICHANG*

This ship displaces 10,000 tons when fully loaded. It is 120 meters long, 18 m wide and its draught is 7 m. She has twin diesel propulsion with two propellers. It reaches a speed of 17.5 knots and has a range of 8,000 miles at 17 knots.

Critical points

Also of importance is the breaking up of some countries that has led to the appearance of new independent states, and those that have sea frontiers have been confronted with the need to build up their own fleets.

As has happened in some cases (Croatia has 32 ships, the Ukraine has 71), many of these ships came directly from the fleets of the countries they previously belonged to. However, many of them have also started building their own ships, either as a way of finding employment for their own industries, or because they are an absolute necessity.

Although the first case may seem rather

unusual, it is not as strange as one might think. This is particularly true of countries that traditionally had a strong naval industry that for one reason or other has found itself thrown into a period of recession and with an insufficient number of orders.

Ambivalent constructions

Generally, a logistic or auxiliary ship is built with civilian parameters that are adapted to determined needs and military uses. That is why the market for this kind of ship has been increasing so much in recent years.

In practice, every navy in the world has a certain number of logistic or auxiliary ships. However, in those whose fleet could not be considered second or even third rate (the US Navy is undoubtedly first rate, and one that parts with the greatest number of vessels), these ships are usually at least second hand, if not more.

Germany

Among the over 100 auxiliary ships of every kind in the Bundesmarine, there are three in particular that are studied here: the Rhön, Glücksburg and Oker; one AOR, one ARL and an AGI.

Rhön

It was built as the *Okene* (Terkol) oiler and purchased in 1976 for conversion by Kröger. It is not armed and has a civilian crew.

AGI *OKER*
At first glance, there would be nothing to suggest that this is a 'spy ship' if it was not for the domes situated over the bridge, one on top of the other, that contain the sensors.

AOL *RHÖN*
These German logistic ships have unusual replenishment points, because they do not have derricks to support the fuel hoses, but instead have a long arm or pole.

Glücksburg

This is a Lüneburg class support ship. It was built by Bremer Vulkan in 1968, and was modernized to maintain military facilities on patrol ships and destroyers, including missile submarines. Some have been taken out of service and sold to Greece and Colombia.

Oker

The three Alster class ships (*Alster, Oste* and *Oker*) were built between 1988 and 1989 and are classified as AGI or intelligence ships, something of a euphemism, because their missions tend to involve listening and studying different radio-telegraphic transmissions.

Australia

The Royal Australian Navy has a total of 31 ships, which could be increased to 47 by including oceanographic and training ships. There are two logistic ships among them: the *Westralia* and the *Success*.

Success

This ship was built in 1986, in Sydney, by Cockatoo Dockyard. It has a cargo capacity for 8,707 tons of DFM, 975 of JP-5, 116 of distilled water, 250 of ammunition (including two SM-1 missiles and Mk 46 torpedos), 57 of provisions and 95 of different spare parts.

It is armed with 40/70-mm CIWS guns, 12.7-mm machine guns, and a helicopter.

Canada

The Royal Canadian Navy lists 26 auxiliary vessels, including the *Preserver* and the *Protecteur,* two almost identical AOR.

Preserver

This ship carries up to 14,590 tons of fuel, 400 of JP-5, 1,048 of dry cargo and 1,250 of ammunition. It has four refuelling points and a pair of 15-ton cranes. Both the *Preserver* and the *Protecteur* are used as staff ships and for troop transport. They can operate with ASW helicopters at the same time as transporting several vehicles and barrelled loads. Since appearing in the Gulf, they have been armed with 76-mm guns, CIWS and 12.7-mm machine guns.

China

The Chinese PLAN (People's Liberation Army Navy) lists nearly two hundred vessels, including the Nancang and Shichang. The former is an AOR/AK and the latter is a training ship.

Nancang

It was built by Kherson, in Crimea, as one of 11 identical ships. The Chinese Dalian shipyard

AOR/AK *NANCANG*

This ship has an unusual stern with an individualistic looking balcony. It has RAS (Refuelling at Sea) facilities, with two points on the sides with large, strong double derricks and a point on the deck at the stern.

AOR *CHUN JEE*

It has four supply points, two on either side, and a VERTREP zone at the stern, but with no hangar. It has three 6-ton hoists. It was probably inspired by the two Italian Strombolis.

received it in 1993, where it was finished off ready for commissioning in 1996.

It is not unlike India's *Jyoti,* although certain facilities have been added for its *Super Frelon* helicopter. It has the capacity for cargos of 9,630 tons of naval fuel.

Shichang

Considered a smaller version of the British *Argus,* this ship can be used as a cargo vessel, container carrier, training ship and hospital. It can be used for training naval officers and pilots thanks to its helicopter spots. It can also be used as a civilian craft.

It accommodates a crew of 170 people and 200 students, and can carry as many as 300 containers.

Colombia

The Colombian navy is an important navy by South American standards. They have 40 auxiliary vessels, including those used on rivers. These include the *Cartagena de Indias* and the *Buenaventura,* both with their origins in the German Bundesmarine.

Buenaventura

Refer back to the *Glücksburg,* because this is a more or less similar *Lüneburg* that was transferred to the Colombian Armada in 1998.

South Korea

This navy has 28 auxiliary ships, amongst which the AOR Chun Jee can be found.

Chun Jee

These are three ships that were made in Korea by Hyundai, Ulsan. They have the capacity for 4,200 tons of liquid fuels and 450 tons of solid cargo. They are armed with Emerlec and Vulcan Gatling guns.

India

The most powerful third world nation possesses 52 auxiliary vessels, including the Jyoti and the Tir.

AOR *FORT VICTORIA*
Six ships were originally going to make up the class, but only two were built. They have points on their sides for liquid and solid replenishment and a fifth at the stern for liquids only. They have facilities for the repair of Merlin helicopters, and can be modified to allow for emergency STOVL airplane landings.

TIR TRAINING SHIP
It can displace 2,400 tons when fully loaded and is 105.9 meters long. It is propelled by two Crossley-Pielstick 8 PC2 V Mk 2 diesel engines, with speeds of 18 knots and a range of 6,000 miles at 12 knots.

Jyoti

It was originally an oiler that was built by the Admiralty shipyard in Saint Petersburg in 1996. It has the capacity for 25,040 tons of fuel.

Tir

This Indian built training ship was to be followed by another, but financial problems got in the way. It accommodates a crew of 239 people, to whom 120 cadets can be added.

Italy

Italy has a total of 117 auxiliary ships, including 32 harbor tugs and 11 for roadsteads. Their AOR are the Etna, Stromboli and Vesuvio.

Stromboli

It was built by Fincantieri in 1975. It has the capacity for 3,000 tons of marine fuel, 1,000 of diesel, 400 of JP-5 and 300 of different cargos.

Pakistan

It has a total of nine auxiliary ships, amongst which figure the Moawin and Nasr, the former Dutch Poolster and Chinese X-350, respectively.

Nasr

It was built in China by Dalian in 1987. It has the capacity for 10,550 tons of marine fuel, 1,000 of diesel, 200 of industrial water and a further 200 of drinking water.

Thailand

Of its 18 auxiliary ships, the most important is the Similan, a specially designed AOR for supporting aircraft carriers and their frigates.

Similan

It was built in 1996, in Shanghai, by Hudong. It has four liquid supply points, two on either side, and a flight deck for VERTREP at the stern. It operates with two Seahawk type helicopters.

Great Britain

The Royal Fleet Auxiliary Service has 23 auxiliary ships of every type, amongst which are the two Fort Victoria: *Fort Victoria* and *Fort George*.

Fort Victoria

With a displacement of 36,580 tons when fully loaded, it is one of the biggest AOR in existence. Its cargo capacity is 12,505 m3 of liquids and 6,234 of solids. She has a mixed crew of 95 members of the RFA, 9 of the RN and 24 civilians, along with 154 members of the air force.

AOR SUCCESS

The project of this ship was based on the French Durance. It has two refuelling points on each side, one capable of dealing with heavy solids. Its two SEMT-Pielstick diesel engines and two Lips propellers give them a speed 20 knots, with a range of 8,616 miles at 15 knots.

AOR NASR

It is similar to the Chinese Fuqing class ships. Despite having three sets of derricks, it only has two refuelling points on each side, because the stern does not have the appropriate installations. It has one solid cargo point on each side. Sometimes it also transports cadets.

Traditionally, the position from which a situation was controlled on a warship was the bridge, or in the case of sailing ships the quarterdeck. However, in the last half century, radar has added another dimension.

The chain of control

Since the dawn of navigation, the Captain was positioned at the stern, the place where the rudder tiller was located because, as these ships were relatively smaller, it was the Captain himself who assumed the role of helmsman.

As ships grew larger, the two roles were separated, as it was no longer possible for the captain or commander, to always be near the steering equipment. At this point, it might be worth clarifying the difference between the steersman, or helmsman, who is in charge of operating the ship's rudder, and the commander, who is the person in charge. Therefore, here we shall use the most modern names and concepts, and hope to avoid confusion with other, now archaic terms.

Ancient rowing boats demanded the presence of somebody who was presumably not too popular with the crew to serve as a slave driver. His main purpose was to regulate the oar strokes, which was done by whipping any oarsman who seemed in any way reticent to do so.

CONSOLES

Modern CIC feature all kinds of consoles, such as that of the *Alcor*, a combat system made by EN Bazán. Its main console is shown in the photograph: on the right, the tactical console; on the left, that for the weapons.

MULTI COMMAND

One single console can have several operators, who serve different functions. Moreover, they have a very reliable mouse-like gadget (the yellow object). In the photo, we can also see the computerized tactical naval treatment.

With the appearance of several masts and increasingly more sophisticated rigging, came the introduction of the second commander (on military vessels) or the first mate (on merchant ships). A second commander was necessary due to the complex nature of handling such ships, and the control of the rudder and the balance of the sails were completely different operations. Other officers were introduced with more specific roles, such as personnel management and the substitution of the commander whenever he was absent. The existence of guns on board meant that the commander needed to rely on the services of another person to take charge of them, the weapons officer.

The appearance of steam brought about the need for yet another person on board who was again properly trained in his craft. At first, this would be a simple mechanic or master, but as the complexity of this propulsion system increased, this person assumed the role of chief engineer.

Nowadays, the tasks on board a warship have become so complex that the commander needs the support of a whole range of subordinates who control each of the

different functions, and he will analyse each one's reports before coming to a decision.

From the deck to the bridge

As the size of ships continued to become larger, it became more difficult for the Captain to see what was going on about him. In time this lead to a new location with better visibility being needed (on sailing ships the rudder is controlled with the sails in sight so as to be able to accurately control direction), as well as a way for the voice of the commander to be carried better.

The arrival of steam put an end to such a need and instead a gangway or bridge was installed near the center of the ship that crossed the vessel from one side to the other. From here, orders could be given and the situation could be controlled more easily. Some say that the term 'bridge' came about because of that, although others may well be right in suggesting that the word has its origins in the French word 'pont' or the Italian 'ponto', which translate to English both as 'deck' and 'bridge'.

MULTI-PURPOSEFULNESS

Modern equipment tries to be as multi-functional as possible to avoid any breakdowns leaving an important sensor inoperative. This photograph shows the CIC of an American AEGIS Baseline III cruiser.

WEAPONS CONSOLES

Weapons consoles are not very different to sensor ones, but offer different information and operate in a different way.

Whatever the reason, the fact is that after a few years, that bridge from where orders were given was raised to the top of a superstructure that contained several decks or levels. The simple reason is that the movement of the ship and other operations, such as fire control, can be observed and controlled better from a height.

Having guns that could be fired as far as the horizon, and the sophistication of modern

The development of artillery

It has been suggested, by respected naval historians, that the first naval gun attack was not, as has been suggested in the past the attack on La Rochela (1372) by Ambrosio Bocanegra, but it was in fact some twelve years earlier in 1359, in a battle between Castillians and Catalans. The shots, of which there were only two, were fired from a ship anchored in the port of Barcelona and were directed towards a Castillian fleet that was personally commanded by King Peter the Cruel.

From the fourteenth century to the present date, naval gunnery has gone through enormous changes, reaching extraordinary levels of accuracy. However, although it was once possible to control fire by eyesight alone, telescopic methods would later be needed, and by the 20th century, when the *Dreadnought* appeared, a high caliber naval gun (305/45 mm Mk X) could reach 11 miles, a distance well beyond the horizon. One would only be able to see the target at such a distance from a considerable height above the sea surface, and therefore the bridge and/or artillery control point had to be at the very top of the ship.

In the Second World War, with fire controlled electronically, the Yamato's 460/45 millimeter

artillery weapons, were an added complication to the commander's workload. He was provided with a bridge that included displays of the most important information, and it was the terminal point of much more on top of that, and the origin of each and every order.

guns could reach as far as 44 km (23.7 miles), using 1,460 kg projectiles. The fire was directed from special compartments that we could accredit as being the first Combat Information Centers.

Radar and the CIC

As the knowledge and use of radar became more widespread, a room started appearing on warships for housing the terminals for all the relevant sensors, especially on larger ships and aircraft carriers. This room came to be known by the name of CIC (Combat Information Center). From there, all the highly important data that was obtained by that electronic system could be transferred to the commander, or maybe the admiral in certain cases.

The cold, dark atmosphere of those rooms was a result of the characteristics of such equipment. The way they operated, originally using valves, and nowadays integrated circuits, raised the temperature of the interior, which was not helped by the stuffy presence of several people. This could cause the machines to have operational problems, and so the use of air conditioning is obligatory. These rooms are always dark or have subdued lighting because of the low amount of light that the monitors give off, particularly

VARYING DIMENSIONS

The bridge is one of the areas that is most adapted to the size and type of ship. In particular, on ships like those with islands, the bridge tends to be somewhat smaller, which also supposes the reduction in size of all the services, panels and controls.

DISPLAY MONITOR

The presentation of information through images has changed a lot over the years. Images can now be shown in much higher resolution. This photo shows the CONTAC (CONsola TÁCtico/Tactical Console) of the *Alcor*.

the earlier models that had yellow phosphorous screens. It was by no means easy to make images out on the screens unless the rooms were dimly lit.

With the advent of the electronic age, the role of the CIC was further increased, and the amount of important information generated was so large that it could not be handed on to the commander in such an extensive form. Therefore, the commander was provided with his own position, usually in the center of the room. From here he could observe and control each and every piece of information that was received. With this new system, and given the volume of information that could be obtained at any given moment, the competency and decision-making prowess of the commander is thoroughly put to the test.

The CIC

There are several monitors in the CIC, usually depending on the ships armament and sensors. They are placed in areas of the room in such a way that each officer in charge of a section has many other source of information at his disposal within the immediate area, thus minimising any kind of movements that would only serve to waste time. For this reason, a CIC is a prime example of operational ability, reasoning and ergonomics, together with the movements and presence of its personnel.

Therefore, the panels and monitors of the

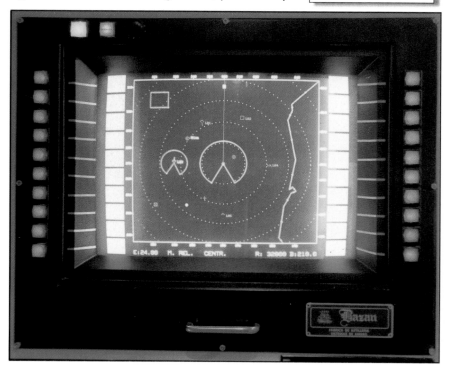

long distance search and reconnaissance equipment are placed in rows, with the operators sitting side by side. Those who control the weapons, guns, CIWS, missiles and so on are also seated near to each other. Only the electronic warfare and anti submarine warfare operators are positioned in an adjacent area, separated only by a curtain.

Other facilities that can be situated near to the CIC, because they are always going to be related in some way or other, are the communication systems, and the different coding apparatus, and the computer room.

The presence of the commander can frequently be required both on the bridge and on the CIC, so the two areas are usually very close together on modern ships. The same can be said for the commander's quarters, which are usually in the vicinity of these two rooms.

The bridge

At the bridge there is one, or sometimes several, monitors that can be used for obtaining information, but in no way is this ever likely to match the size and depth of infor-

COMMANDER'S POSITION

Every CIC has a control position from where the person in charge, responsible for the CIC or the commander himself, can observe and control operations. This position has a high, swivel chair from where the whole area can be observed at a glance.

mation and data that can be produced by the CIC.

Logically, the bridge includes all the different elements that are needed to command a ship, such as the rudder, remote controls for the machinery and stabilising fins, navigation radar and many other features.

INDEX